V-2

V-2

BY

WALTER DORNBERGER

Major General, formerly Commanding Officer of
the Peenemünde Rocket Research Institute

TRANSLATED BY
JAMES CLEUGH AND GEOFFREY HALLIDAY

INTRODUCTION BY
WILLY LEY

NEW YORK · 1954

THE VIKING PRESS

Library of Congress catalog card number: 54-7830

CONTENTS

ILLUSTRATIONS

following page xvi

The author, Dr. Walter Dornberger

A rocket A-3 on Test Stand IV at Kummersdorf West

Test Stand I at Peenemünde

Observer's post, Test Stand I

A model of rocket A-4 (V-2) in the wind tunnel

Dr. Dornberger and Professor Hermann Oberth

Dr. Dornberger and his top engineers

A wooden mock-up of an A-4 on a Meillerwagen

A V-2 on a Vidalwagen for road transportation

One of the first A-4 rockets
  Four seconds after take-off
  Ready for firing at Test Stand VII

A V-2 ready for firing from a special train

Checking instrumentation of a V-2

Liquid-fuel rocket units undergoing acceptance tests

Test Stand VII during preparations for firing an A-4

Big day at Peenemünde—the visit of the Long-Range Bombardment Commission

Heinrich Himmler visits Peenemünde

Himmler and Dr. Dornberger on Test Stand VI

Test Stand VII as photographed by the United States Air Force

INTRODUCTION

BY WILLY LEY

When, on November 10, 1944, Winston Churchill disclosed in Parliament that a German long-range rocket was in action and that such rockets had fallen in the Greater London area for a number of weeks, he ended a long period of rumors of all kinds. Anybody old enough to have read the newspapers at that time will recall that for about a year the press had been in the habit of referring to the French coast between Calais and Cherbourg as the "rocket-gun coast," and that during this time there had been a sensational "disclosure" about the nature of the German "secret weapon" roughly twice a month. These stories, spread by teletype to any newspaper editor who might feel inclined to print them, usually came with a Stockholm or Zürich dateline and told amazing things. One version had it that the new German weapon would utterly destroy an area of 20 square miles with one blow. Another report told of "tons of liquid air," that made artificial icebergs all around southern England. A third writer "knew" that the weapon was a rocket weighing 15 tons which was first lifted by an airplane to a high altitude in order to increase its range. Most of these reports contained scientific or technological absurdities; many of them also looked as if they had been planted by Dr. Goebbels' propaganda forces.

When the first flying bombs crossed the Channel around the middle of June 1944, the riddle of what concrete truth, if any, there was behind all these rumors, seemed solved. But soon after, to be precise, on July 6, 1944, Winston Churchill spoke of an up-to-then completely unknown place called Peenemünde as the "main experiment station both of the flying bomb and the long-range rocket"; adding, "at first our information led us to believe that a rocket weapon would be used." This made it evident that there was a German long-range rocket. Allied Intelligence—but not the public—knew this because, also in June 1944, a long-range rocket had been mistakenly directed toward Sweden and had ended its career in an airburst high over the Kalmar area. If a rocket breaks up in the air its pieces "flutter" to the ground with reasonable gentleness, so that they are not smashed beyond recognition. The Swedes had agreed to hand the pieces over to the Allies and they had been flown to England by an American pilot.

But the question still was whether the rocket would be used operationally. By the time Winston Churchill announced that this was the case—the first V-2 fell at 6:43 p.m., September 8, 1944, at Chiswick, the second 16 seconds later at Epping—the British Air Ministry had not only completed its studies of the wreckage from Sweden but even prepared a detailed release which was carried by the British newspapers the next morning.

The long-rumored "secret weapon" turned out to be a rocket of about 12 tons take-off weight, capable of carrying a payload (warhead) of 1 ton over a range of approximately 200 miles. The surprising thing to the then comparatively small number of people interested in rockets was not that this had been done but how the Germans had managed to do it so fast. Countless people asked me about the size of German rockets as I had known them prior to 1935. I could reply only that the biggest, finished in the spring of 1933, had been about man-sized. The largest of Dr. Robert H. Goddard's rockets, fired on May 31, 1935, at the Mescalero Ranch near Roswell in New Mexico—by coincidence fairly near, as they judge distances in New Mexico, to today's White Sands Proving Ground—had been somewhat taller than the German rocket I had in mind, had weighed a little less, but had reached a height of 7500 feet, while the German example had got stuck in its launching rack.

To create the 46-foot rocket, which had first become known

because of the airburst over Sweden, everybody admitted, must have been an enormous effort. There was also unanimous agreement in scientific and engineering circles that this rocket was one of the major inventions of recorded history. A debate of whether it was also of major military importance was cut short by the new type of explosion over Hiroshima. Whether the rocket with a high-explosive warhead constituted a first-class weapon became an extinct problem; there was now the probability of a new kind of warhead which would make it irresistible.

But behind all the discussions on the nature of this rocket and its future possibilities—one party said, "End of civilization," while another firmly replied, "On the contrary, beginning of space travel"—behind all these discussions and speculations there lingered one question. It was: just what had been going on in that place where the rocket had been developed, in Peenemünde.

A partial answer was supplied by W. G. A. Perring, Fellow of the Royal Aeronautical Society, during a lecture delivered just about one year after the first official announcement, on November 1, 1945, in the Lecture Hall of the Institution of Mechanical Engineers at Storey's Gate, London. It was a very complete description of the rocket, with references to a number of other German developments that would have aroused intense curiosity in every engineer if they had not been overshadowed a few score times by the V-2. But the lecture dealt with the finished product; it did not tell why things were done the way they had been done. To mention just two items that had puzzled me personally for a long time: why was there a set of eighteen burner cups in the head of the V-2 motor? Why this particular number, why not, say, six? And I had wondered all along why there had been external vanes attached to the tail fins of the rocket. The graphite vanes in the exhaust blast did their job well, it seemed, and the external vanes could work only for a comparatively short time, namely, for the half-minute or so when the rocket was fast enough after its slow take-off but still in air dense enough for vanes to do any good. Mr. Perring's lecture told "how," not "why"—which does not mean that the "how" was not welcome information.

In the years that followed there have been a number of excellent publications about the V-2. I am thinking mainly of the four successive Upper Atmosphere Research Reports of the Naval Research Laboratory in Washington, which contained a fine picture of the utilization of V-2 rockets as instrument carriers for the exploration of the outermost tenuous layers of our atmosphere. But there was still nothing about the origin of this rocket. In 1948 two Dutch scientists, Dr. J. M. J. Kooy and Dr. J. W. H. Uytenbogaart, published a work which contained their eye-witness observation of the firing of V-2 rockets from Dutch soil. Very interesting indeed, but still not what I and very many others wanted to know.

One year later there came a small book from Germany. It was a popular book on rockets and space travel, entitled *Kleine Raketenkunde* and written by one Hans K. Kaiser, an old and always active member of the Society for Space Travel which was founded in Germany in 1927. Kaiser had been in Peenemünde, not in an important capacity, it seems, but at least he had been there. And he could tell what he had seen. But this was still not the story of V-2; that had to come from somebody who had been high up in the organization, preferably at the head.

This book is that story. Here all the various items that to an outsider were pieces, some fragmentary, of a gigantic jigsaw puzzle are fully assembled.

As this book explains, the Peenemünde research institute had its origin in a much smaller research station also designated by a place name: Kummersdorf West. This had been the first rocket research station of the German Army. But even Kummersdorf West was not without a background, a background outside the German Army.

As far as their solid-fuel rockets went, the German Army researchers once more revived—with lots of internal resistance, as the reader will discover—an old tradition. Soldiers in the Second World War, as well as their public at home, usually believed that the bombardment rockets they fired (or, as public, saw fired in the newsreels) were something brand-new. They were that, but only in a narrow sense. In a broader sense the Second World War was the third era in which rockets were weapons of war. The first era had begun soon after the introduction of rockets in Europe and had lasted, in round figures, from 1250 to 1400 A.D. The second era began with the first years of the nineteenth century and is linked with the name of the British Captain William Congreve, who reintroduced rockets as a bombardment weapon. That he was successful is shown by the simple fact that only a decade later he was General Sir William Congreve. This second era, however, lasted barely half a century.

Much nonsense was written about a century ago on the question of why the Congreve rockets, and their successors, the Hale rockets, failed to "take hold" on the military scene. The reason can be clearly discerned, as usual, in the light of afterknowledge. These rockets still used the old saltpeter-charcoal-sulfur black-powder as a propelling charge. The fact that such blackpowder rockets are not too safe at any time, and especially not after a period of storage, was an important factor, to be sure. But what counted much more heavily was that each of these rockets had to be made by hand by skilled labor. They could, with an effort, be made in quantity, but they could not be mass-produced, which is an important difference. Mass production became possible in the Second World War because by then propelling charges had been developed which lent themselves to mass production. The chemistry of these charges was not the same on both sides of the battlefront, nor were the methods of mass production. But they all could be, and were, mass-produced.

As regards their liquid-fuel rockets, Kummersdorf West, and later Peenemünde, had little "former art," as the patent law calls it, to go by. But there was a scientific background. In the early days of the present century a Russian high-school teacher, Konstantin E. Ziolkovsky, began to write about rockets of large size, possibly man-carrying and intended for liquid fuels. His ideas were among the earliest, but they remained unknown outside of Russia. Just after the war, in 1920, the American physicist Professor Robert H. Goddard published, under the title *A Method of Reach-*

ing Extreme Altitudes, a rather thorough mathematical treatment of rocket motion. And three years later in Germany, Professor Hermann Oberth followed with another mathematical treatise, complete with suggestions for designs and construction and with special emphasis on the use of liquid fuels. Oberth was the first man to realize clearly that the change from solid to liquid fuels removed whatever size limit is inherent in solid-fuel rockets. When you switch over to liquids, he stated, there is no theoretical limit to the size of a rocket.

It was because of Oberth's book that the German Society for Space Travel was founded, the first of the many rocket societies now in existence in many countries. The Society for Space Travel tried to raise the money actually to build liquid-fuel rockets. It finally accomplished this, and at that time if such a rocket worked at all, it was "success" enough.

But all this merely proved that the liquid-fuel rocket was not inherently impossible. All the real work was still ahead—mountains of work, which needed an army of qualified experts and, it may be added, also mountains of money.

The way history ran in this case, the mountains of money were supplied, reluctantly, by the German Armed Forces. And the army of qualified men was assembled, slowly and under difficulties, by the author of this book.

The place where the work was done has already been mentioned. What follows tells how it all came about.

FOREWORD

The memoirs of soldiers are generally controversial. War memoirs, especially those of a loser, often serve only one purpose—a more or less "adjusted" interpretation of historical events from the author's point of view.

This book is certainly conditioned by the author's outlook and by the nature and extent of his own experiences, as any factual account must be when it is written with limited access to official documents. Thorough historical research based on full documentation and evidence gathered from interrogation of the participants may conceivably throw a different light on these events. For the understanding of historical actions, however, only the facts known to the protagonists themselves at the moment of their decision are in the last resort valid.

I decided to write this book because it deals with an invention which is certain to exercise a decisive influence on the future of mankind. I have tried to set down everything necessary to an understanding of the development in Germany of the liquid-fuel rocket between 1930 and 1945, including the circumstances in which we lived, worked, and achieved our successes, and finally the end of it all.

After the war a host of contradictory, confusing, and misleading books and articles were published on German rocket development. I do not know where the self-styled experts drew their information. The time now seems ripe to end the confusion and correct mistaken ideas once for all.

I hope that this book will be received in the spirit in which it was written—that is, as the report of a man who for more than ten years had the honor to lead a high-class research group of scientists, engineers, and skilled workers, performing a technological feat of utmost importance for the future.

We have led our generation to the threshold of space—the road to the stars is now open.

Autumn, 1952   Dr. Walter Dornberger

ACKNOWLEDGMENTS

The author wishes to acknowledge the editorial cooperation of F. N. Neher on the original manuscript. The translators are indebted to A. V. Cleaver for much technical help. Further technical help on the American edition was supplied by Willy Ley.

The author, Dr. Walter Dornberger

A rocket A-3 mounted for static firing in Test Stand IV at Kummersdorf West,
Spring 1936

Test Stand I at Peenemünde. The first of the big rocket-motor test stands, designed for motors with thrust up to 100 tons

(*Above*) Observer's post in Test Stand I, Fall 1939. Periscope is at upper left

(*Below*) A model of rocket A-4 (V-2) being tested in the wind tunnel. Shock waves are visible at nose and fins

(*Above*) Dr. Dornberger and Professor Hermann Oberth

(*Below*) Dr. Dornberger and his top engineers in Vienna, Summer 1942. Left to right: Dr. Dornberger, Colonel Zanssen, Dr. Thiel, Dr. von Braun

(*Above*) A wooden mock-up of an A-4 on a Meillerwagen, February 1942. The firing table, with blast deflector, is attached to the tail fins of the mock-up

(*Below*) A V-2 on a Vidalwagen for road transportation, Summer 1944

One of the first A-4 rockets, June 1943

(*Right*) Four seconds after take-off from Test Stand VII. Picture taken from Test Stand I

Ready for firing at Test Stand VII

A V-2 ready for firing from a special train, January 1945

Checking instrumentation of a V-2 just before take-off

(*Above*) Liquid-fuel rocket units developed to assist the take-off of heavy aircraft, undergoing acceptance tests at Peenemünde, May 1940

(*Below*) Test Stand VII during preparations for firing an experimental A-4, October 1943. Picture taken from Test Stand I

Big day at Peenemünde—the visit of the Long-Range Bombardment Commission to decide upon the relative merits of the V-1 and the V-2, May 26, 1943. Left to right, Dr. Thiel, Privy Councilor Plendel, Colonel Count Stauffenberg, General Olbricht (Infantry), Grand Admiral Doenitz, General Brandt (Artillery), Dr. Dornberger, Dr. von Braun

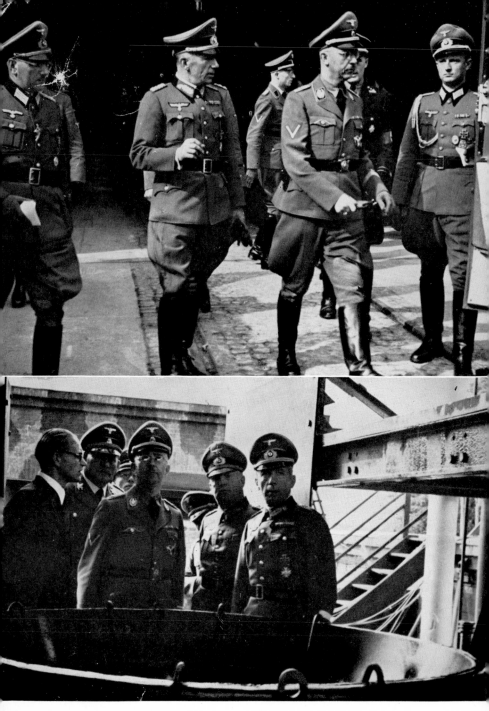

(*Above*) Heinrich Himmler, Reichführer SS, visits Peenemünde

(*Below*) Himmler and Dr. Dornberger on Test Stand VI

Above) Test Stand VII as photographed by the United States Air Force.
... A V-2 on its Meillerwagen. B. A mobile test stand. C. The assembly hall for mobile test stands, where finished V-2's were stored. N—north.

Below) Peenemünde during the air raid of August 17, 1943, photographed by the United States Air Force.

A launching rack at Kummersdorf for heavy solid-fuel rockets (*Do-Werfer* or *Wurfgerät*) being demonstrated to Field Marshal Rommel, Summer 1942

Above) A *Wasserfall* antiaircraft rocket being fired from Test Stand IX at Peenemünde, Fall 1944

Right) An A-4b, forerunner of the A-9, prior to firing from Test Stand X, January 1945

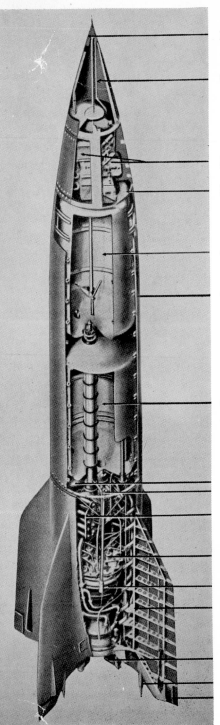

FUZE

WARHEAD

ROCKET INSTRUMENTATION

BULKHEAD

ALCOHOL TANK

CYLINDRICAL CENTER SECTION

OXYGEN TANK,
ALCOHOL PIPE IN CENTER

HYDROGEN-PEROXIDE (H_2O_2) TANK
TURBOPUMP
PRESSURE FLASKS

INJECTION HEADS

COMBUSTION CHAMBER

FIN

INTERNAL (GRAPHITE) VANES

AERIAL
EXTERNAL VANES

CROSS SECTION OF THE V-2
(For additional data see the table on page xvii)

CHARACTERISTICS OF THE ROCKET A-4 (V-2)

	METRIC	U.S.
Length	14 m	46 ft
Diameter of body	1.65 m	5 ft 5 in
Diameter over fins	3.55 m	11 ft 8 in
Weight, empty but with warhead	4000 kg	8818 lb
Take-off weight	12,900 kg	28,440 lb
Payload	1000 kg	2205 lb
High explosive carried	750 kg	1654 lb
Alcohol (containing 25% water)	3965 kg	8740 lb
Oxygen, liquid	4970 kg	10957 lb
Fuel consumption, per second	127 kg	280 lb
Mixture ratio (alcohol/oxygen)	0.81	0.81
Burning time (max)	65 sec	65 sec
Thrust at take-off	25,000 kg	55,100 lb
Thrust gain near Brennschluss	4200 kg	13,230 lb
Acceleration at take-off (effective)	0.9 g	0.9 g
Acceleration at Brennschluss (effective)	5 g	5 g
Temperature in motor	~2700° C	~4890° F
Pressure in motor	15.45 atm	227 lb/sq in
Injection pressure (above motor pressure)	2.4 atm	35.3 lb/sq in
Nozzle expansion ratio	15.45:0.85	15.45:0.85
Exhaust velocity	2050 m/sec	6725 ft/sec
Rocket stays vertical after take-off for	4 sec	4 sec
completes tilt within	50 sec	50 sec
attains angle of 49° from vertical at	54 sec	54 sec
passes speed of sound after	25 sec	25 sec

Velocity along trajectory (max)	1600 m/sec	1 mi/sec
Impact velocity	900–1100 m/sec	3000–3600 ft/sec
Height at Brennschluss	22 km	13.7 mi
Distance from take-off point at Brennschluss	24 km	15 mi
Apogee of trajectory	80–90 km	50–56 mi
Range (max)	320 km	199 mi

V-2

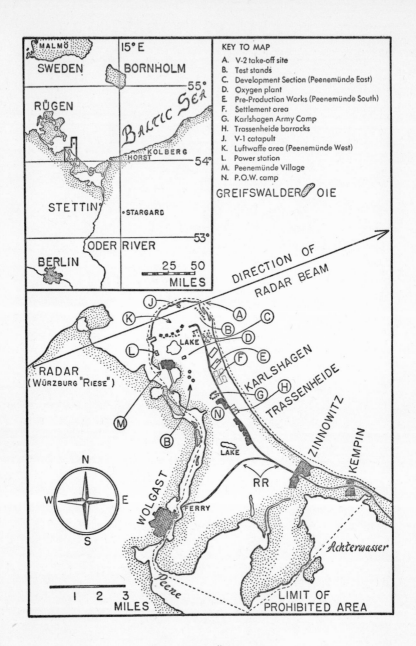

KEY TO MAP
A. V-2 take-off site
B. Test stands
C. Development Section (Peenemünde East)
D. Oxygen plant
E. Pre-Production Works (Peenemünde South)
F. Settlement area
G. Karlshagen Army Camp
H. Trassenheide barracks
J. V-1 catapult
K. Luftwaffe area (Peenemünde West)
L. Power station
M. Peenemünde Village
N. P.O.W. camp

THE PEENEMÜNDE AREA

CHAPTER 1

OCTOBER 3, 1942—"ROCKET AWAY!"

The order had been given. I put down the hand microphone that had carried my words over the intercom system connecting Test Stand VII, the firing command post, and the measurement centers. I was standing on the flat roof of the Measurement House. It was noon, and a clear, cloudless sky arched over North Germany. My eyes strayed out to the Development Works, gloomy in their camouflage, to the spreading pine forests, and across the reedy promontory of the hook of Peenemünde to the island called the Greifswalder Oie, six miles away.

In the south, nestling in the evergreen forest, I saw the two big bright concrete sheds of the Pre-Production Works, their northward-pointing roofs covered with camouflage netting. In the west the low hills on the far bank of the river Peene were dominated by the red-brick tower of Wolgast Cathedral. The light-blue contours of the oxygen-generating plant, almost invisible under their camouflage nets, the six conspicuous chimneys of the big harbor power station, and the long hangars of the Peenemünde air force base completed the picture I had grown to know so well.

The roof of the Measurement House with its protective brick parapet was an ideal observation post. On that October noon I had but a single thought. Would the launching be successful this time? Had we really discovered the cause of failure of the last two attempts, on June 13 and August 16? Were the steps we had taken adequate? Would success today, October 3, 1942, crown our efforts at last and reward our ten years' toil and trouble? A

3

great deal depended on this launching; we all knew that. I was not alone in my anxiety. Engineer Colonel Zanssen stood beside me, his elbows propped on the rampart, surveying the distant scene through his Zeiss glasses with forced calm. I noticed that he looked particularly hard and long northward, where nothing whatever was to be seen. His thoughts also seemed to wander along the paths of his worries. As commanding officer of Army Experimental Station Peenemünde he bore a responsibility which would rest less heavily on him only if we suceeded in our attempt today. The responsibility of success or failure was, however, mine.

To ease the tension of the moment I spoke to Zanssen. As he turned his clear blue eyes upon me I noticed how pale he was. I was impelled to say something encouraging. "Keep your fingers crossed! It must come off this time; there's so much at stake!"

Zanssen merely smiled faintly and leveled his glasses again. What other reply could he have made? I too lifted my binoculars. On the almost flat roof of the green-painted assembly building of the firing site I could see people running to and fro. The photographers and film cameramen were in readiness there, 100 feet up, with the measurement engineers and test-stand staff.

I knew that all was ready in the observation and measurement shelters of the test stand. The engineers were on their toes. Switching procedure had been well rehearsed. Dr. Thiel, in charge of the test area, had devised a master timetable, a schedule that had to be followed exactly. Vigilant eyes were glued to the periscopes built into the thick roof of the concrete shelter, watching the engineers busy with final preparations at the launching site.

The rocket, an A-4—later called V-2, under which name it was to be recorded in history—stood ready on its firing table. It was still connected by two umbilical cables to the measuring instruments in the shelter and to the electric power supply. The senior propulsion and guidance engineers stood at their indirectly lit switchboards in the shelter. They were taking readings from the many measuring instruments, the different kinds of manometers, frequency gauges, voltmeters and ampmeters, watching the green, red, and white signal lamps light up and keeping their hands on the switches, ready to cut in when the signal to start was given. In a separate corner engineers from the firm of Siemens were busy with the precision focusing of a television camera. Telephones shrilled. The nasal tones of loudspeakers were heard emitting telephone conversations among the launching-control staff, the measurement centers, the fire-control people, and the engineer in charge of power supply.

At last the final circuit tests, the switching sequence dry run, the checking of all electrically worked stabilization and guiding mechanisms, of all important valves, of pressure chambers and pipes, came to an end. I had no doubt that all this procedure, well rehearsed during many static tests, would go like clockwork. I glanced once more over to the roof of the assembly workshop of the Development Works, on which were assembled Colonel Stegmaier, military commander of the Development Works and in charge of fire control, Dr. von Braun, chief of engineering, and Dr. Steinhoff, head of the mysterious Department of Instruments, Guidance, and Measurement. Slightly apart from this group I could see the supersonic wind-tunnel staff. I recognized Dr. Hermann and Dr. Kurzweg. They had the special task of observing the rocket in flight through ten-power binocular periscopes, and dictating their comments independently; their clerks stood ready beside them.

When I leaned over the parapet I could see a great deal of animated action. In the avenues and paths among the widely scattered buildings of the works, at the windows and on the roofs of sheds, workshops, and offices, the entire staff seemed to be waiting and watching. There would have been no point in forbidding any of the people who had worked together for years on developing the A-4 to share in the show. All wanted to witness the event they had striven for, one that would perhaps make history. I was quite sure I could rely on the human element; these people would not fail me.

The steering gyroscopes in the rocket were now running. From the loudspeaker connected with the intercom system came the first rumbling announcement: "X minus three."

There were still 3 minutes to go. Those 3 minutes! Their almost unbearable tension was repeated with every test run or firing, and they gradually came to be known as the "Peenemünde minutes." They always seemed so much longer than 60 seconds.

The television engineers had finished adjusting their apparatus. The softly glowing screen showed the slender, perfect body of the rocket, lacquered black and white, and glittering in the clear sunlight. Thus and not otherwise must be the shape of the projectile that would meet the heavy demands we should be making on it. This rocket had to go through the sound barrier. The slender sharp-pointed nose took on the shape of a Gothic arch as it joined the cylindrical body. The four fins of the conically narrowing stern divided the body into four parts, lacquered in different colors to facilitate the evaluation of the pictures to be taken. A broad white band of condensed atmospheric moisture encircled the rocket at the level of the liquid oxygen tank. Oxygen vapor streamed from the open vent valve at the stern, forming evanescent little balls of cloud on contact with the moisture of the air.

The working platforms were withdrawn. The staff had taken refuge in the shelters. The rocket was now isolated. Vaporization suddenly ceased. I knew that the vent valve had been closed by remote control. I could almost feel the rise of pressure in the oxygen tank.

"X minus one."

The tension mounted. How often I had put my nerves to the test up here these last 6 months! How often had the trial had to be abandoned at the last moment and the order to fire canceled because of some technical failure! On that third of October, 1942, I could feel no surprise that even leading Peenemünde men had doubted whether an operational weapon could ever be made of the long-range rocket. So far we had succeeded only twice in getting a rocket of this size off the ground at all. We had had two unsuccessful firings. All our theories had still not stood the test of practice. We knew only one thing: we must not fail today. This was the final verdict.

It seemed to me that in this war we had been tying brilliant men and much good material to an unproved idea too long. Already we had competitors who promised to achieve, at less cost, what we had set out to do. Could I in the circumstances take the responsibility for continuing? Months had gone by without any visible signs of progress. If today's trial failed I should be forced to report to higher authority that we had been wrong. As I had borne sole responsibility for the undertaking for more than ten years, I should be the one to take the consequences; and I should have to propose the transfer of all our armament potential to aircraft or tank construction.

I felt cold with suspense and excitement under the warm autumn sun; I was glad I was alone with my friend Colonel Zanssen and not exposed to the critical scrutiny of my staff.

There seemed no end to that last minute. I had to suppress a longing to look at my watch and count the seconds. Though a thousand questions demanding instant answers rushed through my mind, I had to control myself and not disturb the preparations worked out to the last tiny detail. That was a real "Peenemünde minute."

A smoke shell hissed into the sky. Its green track over Test Stand VII drifted sluggishly away before the wind. Ten seconds more! The picture on the television screen was unchanged.

"Ignition!"

The propulsion engineer must have pulled the first of the three main switches. I noticed on the television picture that clouds were issuing from the nozzle mouth. Sparks shot through them, bounced off the blast deflector, and scattered over the concrete platform on which the firing table stood.

"Preliminary stage!"

The rain of sparks rapidly coalesced to a flame and changed within a second to a jutting jet of reddish-yellow combustion gases. The flame of the 8-ton thrust of the preliminary stage developed. The power of this preliminary stage was not yet sufficient to lift the 13.5-ton rocket from the firing table. The preliminary stage was scheduled to last 3 seconds. Smoke began to darken the picture. Ends of cables, pieces of wood, and bits of grass flew through the air. I saw the cables detach themselves from the rocket and fall downward. At the same moment the rocket instrumentation was switched over to its internal batteries. The guiding mechanism now received current from its own source.

"Rocket has lifted!"

The propulsion engineer had pulled the third and last main lever. Release of the casting-off cables ushered in the main stage. A turbopump of 4000 revolutions per minute and a capacity of 540 horsepower came into play, forcing 33 gallons of alcohol and oxygen per second into the combustion chamber of the rocket motor with an injection pressure exceeding the pressure inside the motor by 44 pounds per square inch.

After about a second, thrust rose to 25 tons. With an acceleration practically corresponding to that of a falling stone, the rocket climbed straight and steadily upward from the launching table and disappeared from the television screen, leaving behind it an immense whirling cloud of dust.

I kept my eyes glued to the binoculars and looked north. The gleaming body of the rocket rose vertically from the forest into the sky.

It was an unforgettable sight. In the full glare of the sunlight the rocket rose higher and higher. The flame darting from the stern was almost as long as the rocket itself. The fiery jet of gas was clear-cut and self-contained. The rocket kept to its course as though running on rails; the first critical moment had passed. Missile A-4 had shown itself to be stable about its longitudinal axis. The projectile was not spinning; the black and white surface markings facing us did not change.

The air was filled with a sound like rolling thunder, the roar of the rocket motor just reaching us. We heard the preliminary stage first and the main one a few seconds later. The sound had covered a distance of 1500 yards before our ears registered its power. Only 5 seconds had passed since ignition of the preliminary stage. The thunderous rumble increased. The combustion gases shot out of the exhaust nozzle at a speed of over 6500 feet per second, having reached a temperature of about 5100 degrees

Fahrenheit in the combustion chamber. The energy released was truly gigantic; the combustion chamber generated over 650,000 horsepower at the end of the burning time.

The rocket held to its vertical course for only 4.5 seconds, then it began, almost imperceptibly at first, to incline its tip eastward. The tilt had begun.

I followed breathlessly the dramatic rush of the flying projectile as it sped faster and faster on its course, and its slow, steady inclination from the vertical to the angle of 50 degrees required for maximum range. From my position on the roof of the Measurement House I had a particularly clear side view of this part of the trajectory.

As I stared upward through my binoculars I suddenly became aware that, besides the rhythmic rise and fall of the rushing and roaring of the rocket motor, other sounds were reaching my ears, some steady, some changing in pitch. I listened with attention. The timekeeper of Launching Control was monotonously counting out the seconds of flight through the loudspeaker: "Fourteen . . . fifteen . . . sixteen . . . seventeen . . ."

At the same time I heard from the second loudspeaker the continuous tone of the measuring pitch. This gave the result, rendered acoustically, of electronic measurement of the rocket's speed. Rising steadily from a deep hum to a shrill piping, its tone pierced ever more clearly the reverberating roar of the motor.

On the far bank of the Peene, about 7.5 miles from the launching site in the direct line of flight, stood the high-frequency transmitter of the Brennschluss [1] equipment. From the moment of launching, the equipment's directional antenna transmitted its short wave toward the missile as the latter rose higher and higher.

"Nineteen . . . twenty . . . twenty-one . . ."

The rocket sped faster and faster on its thunderous way. Its velocity was now something like 650 miles per hour. In the next few seconds it would reach the speed of sound.

---

[1] Literally: "end of burning"; the German word is preferred to the form "all-burnt," which is used in England, because at Brennschluss considerable quantities of fuel may still be left in the tanks.

"Sonic velocity!" reported the loudspeaker at last. My heart missed a beat. Now was the time—what if the white cloud of an explosion should appear in the blue sky?

Nothing appeared. The missile flew on imperturbably, as though nothing had happened. Yet at that moment on the third of October, 1942, supersonic speed was achieved for the first time by a liquid-propellant rocket. An old dream of mankind, whose significance engineers had been slow to recognize, had found its realization. This clear proof that a fin-stabilized rocket projectile could remain stable through the sound barrier and at supersonic speeds relieved me of one of my worst anxieties.

"Twenty-nine . . . thirty . . . thirty-one . . ."

The measurement tone grew steadily clearer and higher, sounding louder and louder above the fainter rumble of the missile as it passed farther into the distance at increasing supersonic speed. The rocket remained distinctly visible through the binoculars, the reddish gleam of its trail of flame conspicuous against the deep blue sky.

"Thirty-three . . . thirty-four . . . thirty-five . . ."

The tilt of the rocket, now foreshortened from below, seemed considerably more acute. The missile was traveling away at visibly increasing speed. By now it must be 6 miles high and have reached a Mach number of 2—that is, twice the speed of sound; the measurement tone proclaimed the fact. I became utterly absorbed in the remarkable picture presented by the shining flame and the glittering black and white of the projectile.

"Thirty-eight . . . thirty-nine . . . forty . . ."

A paralyzing shock! A trail of white had appeared in the clear blue sky. I heard people shouting, "An explosion!"

A deep, almost genial voice declared through the loudspeaker, "Nonsense! That's the oxygen vent opening."

"No, I saw it. The fins have come off! Look at them—there they go!"

"Rubbish! That's vaporization."

"She's falling!"

A babble of voices arose. But the measurement tone came calmly and steadily from the loudspeakers. The increasing speed of the rocket was clearly audible. It was leaving behind it, owing to condensation of the combustion gases, a long, snow-white vapor trail.

"She's turning over!"

"She's off her course! The vapor trail's jagged!"

"No, she's flying on!"

Here was man's first sight of a phenomenon that was later to grow so familiar—"frozen lightning." The varying air currents through which the rocket rushed at different heights at a speed of over 2000 miles per hour caused the vapor trail to run zigzag. What diversity of air currents and what tremendous wind velocities there must be at that height to cause such visible distortion of the condensation streak in a matter of seconds!

"Forty-nine . . . fifty . . . fifty-one . . ."

The measurement tone was now a shrill piping. The Brennschluss stage must soon come.

To reach the calculated range the rocket would have to fulfil three fundamental requirements at Brennschluss, that is, the combustion end-point of its course. First, it must be on the right course. This was arranged by a precision measuring instrument known to all land surveyors, the theodolite. By turning the rocket on the firing table, an axis of the gyroscopic guiding system was accurately laid off in the direction required. Second, the rocket must have reached the calculated speed. This was continuously measured by Doppler radar, and at the right moment the Brennschluss equipment would automatically switch off the rocket motor by the same means. Third, at the prescribed height the rocket must form a specific tangent with the calculated curve of the trajectory. This was taken care of by the programmed automatic guidance system which directed the rocket into its correct tilt. In addition we could accurately plot the trajectory by means of a complicated radar measuring system which included a transmitter built into the rocket.

"Fifty-two . . . fifty-three . . ."

A sudden thought flashed through my mind. Not long before

the war scientific periodicals had in all seriousness raised the question whether the top layers of our atmosphere might not consist of a mixture of oxygen and hydrogen. If so, there should be a tremendous bang in a few seconds. We are still waiting for it.

To the naked eye nothing was visible of the rocket any more except the vapor trail and a tiny reddish dot indicating its nose. The loudspeakers relentlessly delivered the count of the timekeeper and the high whine of the measurement tone. Behind this there was the strangely fluctuating roar of the rocket motor. With my powerful glasses I could still see the rocket sharply in the clear air, now 20 miles away.

"Fifty-four . . ."

"Brennschluss!" a voice called. The glowing point of the gas jet ceased to be visible in the less powerful binoculars, yet the rocket had not stopped burning, for with my strong glasses I could still see a reddish flame, though a considerably shorter one, darting from the exhaust. The measurement note was still climbing, though slowly.

"Fifty-seven . . . fifty-eight . . ."

Only now had the Brennschluss equipment closed the last valves by radio. The reddish flame had vanished. The thick white vapor trail was forming no longer. Only a thin, milky streak of mist still followed the rocket as it raced away at a speed close to 3500 miles per hour. I could still make out a tiny dot glittering dazzlingly white at the end of a small dark streak. These were the white-hot graphite vanes. The measurement note hovered at an almost uniform pitch.

Taking a deep breath, I put down my binoculars. My heart was beating wildly. The experiment had succeeded. For the first time in the history of the rocket we had sent an automatically controlled rocket missile to the border of the atmosphere at Brennschluss and put it into practically airless space. We had been working ten years for this day.

I am not ashamed to admit that I wept with joy. I couldn't speak for a moment; my emotion was too great. I could see that

Colonel Zanssen was in the same state. He was standing there laughing. His eyes were moist. He stretched out his hands to me. I grasped them. Then our emotions ran away with us. We yelled and embraced each other like excited boys. I don't know whether anyone was watching us, or whether others caught the mood from us, but everyone was shouting, laughing, leaping, dancing, and shaking hands. It's still a matter of surprise to me that no one fell off those crowded roofs. I dashed downstairs to my car to drive to the assembly workshop and thence to Test Stand VII and the fellow workers who had stood by me so long. It was they who were primarily responsible for our success. I left the roof of the Measurement House with the note still ringing in my ears at constant pitch; the timekeeper's monotonous voice still mingled with the faraway hollow rumble of the rocket motor. "Eighty-nine . . . ninety . . . ninety-one . . . ninety-two . . ."

As I went out into the street half the technical staff came dashing toward me. There was much handshaking. I bundled von Braun into the car and drove at reprehensible speed to Test Stand VII. As we shot through the open gate in the sand walls surrounding the great arena we beheld something like a popular riot. The test field crews had surrounded Dr. Thiel and the chief engineers. Everyone wanted to communicate his own particular observations and experiences. As I got out I caught sight of the firing table and the working platforms with the cast-off cables hanging from them. I saw the effect produced in the immediate neighborhood of the launching place by the powerful gases which had scorched and swept aside everything in their course. That was of no consequence. We had learned a great deal that would help us with further development and the tactics of launching. I can still see Thiel's face, with his shrewd savant's eyes sparkling behind his thick spectacles. He was sucking an aged, extinct pipe, and his response to my congratulations was a flood of new ideas and suggestions for improvement. He was seen that very same night at his desk, working at reports and observations. He was never still, never rested and never relaxed.

As I grasped innumerable hands I still had an ear for the

piping measurement tone, sounding here too, and the voice of the timekeeper.

"Two-ninety-one . . . two-ninety-two . . . two-ninety-three . . ."

The pitch still seemed as high as it had been some minutes earlier. No one else was listening; everyone was still far too excited. Most were content with the fact that the launching had gone without a hitch. I had to call for quiet, for the experiment was not yet over. In a few seconds the rocket, traveling at well over 3000 miles per hour, would re-enter the earth's atmosphere. It would be braked down to about 2000 miles per hour by the rapidly increasing air friction. How often had we debated that dangerous stage of the trajectory! We still did not know whether the rocket would withstand the stresses. What would happen if heating of the skin to almost 1250 degrees Fahrenheit, as measured in the wind tunnel, caused the outer metal skin to peel off? The rocket would be torn to pieces long before it reached the ground.

There it came! The measurement tone fell rapidly until at last it sounded as though air were escaping from a toy balloon.

"Two-ninety-four . . . two-ninety-five . . . two-ninety-six . . ."

Impact!

The measurement tone had ceased.

We looked at each other and knew: now, and only now, could we say our experiment had been successful. The rocket had struck the earth with an impact energy of 1400 million foot-pounds, corresponding to that of fifty express-train engines, each weighing a hundred tons, and hitting an obstacle simultaneously at 60 miles per hour.

After I had spent some time listening to the engineers' reports we drove to the Measurement House to sum up the experiment. Charts stretched over large wooden frames recorded the course of the missile, which had flown roughly eastward across the bay of Swinemünde and continued about 20 miles north of the Pomeranian coast. Besides the firing point the charts showed the locations of the trajectory measuring points and the cinetheodolite stations for optical measurement of the first, propelled stage of the trajectory. On arrival we were told by Flight Captain Dr. Steinhoff that the point of impact would probably be found 125 miles away. Steinhoff left immediately afterward in a Messerschmitt Me-111 to reconnoiter.

As we always fired out to sea, our rockets contained bags of dyes that would leave on the water a large bright green stain easily recognizable from the air. As soon as the aircraft, flying at a great height, spotted the stain, it would radio a cruising motor launch to the place to plot the point of impact. The aircraft would then take rough bearings on a known point on the coast and return to Peenemünde.

I recalled the time when Steinhoff had literally run into me. On a spring day in 1939 I had driven over to Test Stand I for a static test, and was about to go back when to my astonishment I was suddenly accosted by a young man apparently in his late twenties, who seized my hands with every appearance of genuine enthusiasm and exclaimed, "Sir, you must take me! I'm all yours! I want to stay!"

Not only was this enthusiastic youth entirely unknown to me, but the area of the test stands was then about the most restricted in the whole of Peenemünde. Fortunately von Braun came running up and the thing turned out to be another of his surprises. He had met Steinhoff, who was about to take on a well-paid job, at a conference at the Glider Institute at Darmstadt Technical High School, and after sizing him up had invited him to Peenemünde, telling him he ought to look round there first. Steinhoff had been smuggled in to a static firing of a 25-ton motor on Test Stand I. This never failed to make a shattering impression on any visitor, and Steinhoff had also been impressed by the large-scale modern equipment, the freedom to work, and the prospects of the rocket. We never regretted having taken him into our band of workers. Moreover, he drew a whole train of skilled scientists after him, so that his department developed into a particularly effective one.

Emerging into the sunlight from the semidarkness of the hut entrance, I saw hurrying toward me Professor Oberth, the originator of modern rocket theory and author of *Die Rakete zu den Planet-enräumen*, published in 1923. Oberth is a Transylvanian Saxon. A tragic fate and lack of appreciation of the feasibility of his ideas had prevented him from taking part in the development of the long-range rockets he had prophesied. We all knew how much our work had derived, from the very start, from his pioneering spirit. As he congratulated me, I could only say that the day on which we had been privileged to take the first step into space must also be a day of success and rejoicing for him, and that the congratulations should go to him for showing us the way.

That evening after Steinhoff returned I held a little celebration. I did not dream that our modest party on that lucky third of October would constitute the last happy hours we should spend together. It is a good thing we cannot read what fate has in store for us. Inspired by our successful day and future prospects, I delivered a little panegyric to my small band of intimate colleagues.

"The history of technology will record that for the first time a machine of human construction, a five-and-a-half-ton missile, covered a distance of a hundred and twenty miles with a lateral deflection of only two and a half miles from the target. Your names, my friends and colleagues, are associated with this achievement. We did it with automatic control. From the artilleryman's point of view, the creation of the rocket as a weapon solves the problem of the weight of heavy guns. We are the first to have given a rocket built on the principles of aircraft construction a speed of thirty-three hundred miles per hour by means of rocket propulsion. Acceleration throughout the period of propulsion was no more than five times that of gravity, perfectly normal for maneuvering of aircraft. We have thus proved that it is quite possible to build piloted missiles or aircraft to fly at supersonic speed, given the right form and suitable propulsion. Our automatically controlled and stabilized rocket has reached heights never touched by any man-made machine. Since the tilt was not carried to completion our rocket today reached a height of nearly sixty miles. We have thus broken the world altitude record of twenty-five miles

previously held by the shell fired from the now almost legendary
Paris Gun.

"The following points may be deemed of decisive significance
in the history of technology: we have invaded space with our
rocket and for the first time—mark this well—have used space as
a bridge between two points on the earth; we have proved rocket
propulsion practicable for space travel. To land, sea, and air may
now be added infinite empty space as an area of future intercontinental traffic, thereby acquiring political importance. This
third day of October, 1942, is the first of a new era in transportation, that of space travel. . . .

"So long as the war lasts, our most urgent task can only be the
rapid perfecting of the rocket as a weapon. The development of
possibilities we cannot yet envisage will be a peacetime task. Then
the first thing will be to find a safe means of landing after the
journey through space. . . ."

During the night, which had fallen dark and heavy over Peenemünde, I looked back over the twelve years in which I had been
head of the Army's rocket development. It had been a weary way,
the way of all invention. We had made the grade. Surely, I
thought, it was now safe to assume that in view of a three-year-old
war we would be supplied from now on with all the material, resources, and manpower we needed to begin mass production of
the A-4 at the earliest possible moment. I was mistaken.

CHAPTER 2

ROCKETS, THE TREATY OF
VERSAILLES, AND THE ARMY
WEAPONS DEPARTMENT

Flight into space, flight to the stars by one means or another, is an ancient dream of mankind. No one knows who first thought of rocket propulsion as a way of realizing the dream. It is on record that the Chinese made powder rockets many centuries ago. It is not even possible to say with certainty who first gave expression to the idea of using liquids of high-energy content instead of powder for propulsion in airless space. Only one thing is sure: any ambition to penetrate into space with liquid-propellant rockets was no more than wishful thinking until general technological progress provided the means for realization. Essential prerequisites were the large-scale production of aluminum alloys; the ability to produce, and store, liquid oxygen in quantity or, alternatively, to obtain big supplies of chemicals containing oxygen; and finally the development of electrical and mechanical precision instruments.

Innumerable inventors appeared and were submerged again in the ranks of the misunderstood and the unsuccessful. Some left good ideas behind, a very few did pioneer work and brought minor problems nearer to solution, but all without exception were denied ultimate success.

Like the automobile, the big long-range rocket capable of penetrating space was first made in Germany. Precisely the same fate befell it as befell nuclear fission of the atom with its train of experiments to guide nuclear energy into peaceful channels. The invention of the guided missile and the splitting of the atom both took place in war years. Research workers were obliged to serve the ends of war.

Ever since artillery existed military strategists have dreamed of an ideal projectile with a greater range than the shell. Even while the airplane was entering on its triumphant career, the strategists began to want some carrier of explosive that would be still cheaper to manufacture and simpler to service than, say, a bomber. The V-2 met this requirement.

The Treaty of Versailles restricted Germany in all branches of armament. Only a certain number of troops with weapons of a prescribed caliber might be maintained. Armament factories were subject to severe limitation. The consequence, logically enough, was that the Army Weapons Department began to look for new developments in armament which would increase the fighting power of the few existing troops without violating the Treaty. The international connections of heavy industry, however, made it practically impossible to work at any new secret weapon development without foreign countries becoming aware of it.

Rocket literature revived again in the thirties and experiments drew attention to alleged improvements. The Army Weapons Department, especially the Ballistics and Munitions Branch under Professor Becker (later General Becker), began to take an interest in these ideas, in conjunction with what later became the Research Branch. A report was made to the Minister of National Defense, and toward the end of 1929 it was decided to undertake research on the possibility of using rocket propulsion for military purposes.

The department's initial object was to study the performance and principle of the powder rocket and to develop a light, cheap weapon, easy to produce, which would fire a concentration of rockets carrying the heaviest charge possible against targets of limited area—within 3 to 5 miles. As for the liquid-propellant rocket, the laws of propulsion were first to be verified, safety in working ensured, and the theoretical performance of the missile achieved in practice. A preliminary model was to be built for study and experiment.

In the spring of 1930, after finishing my technical studies, I was appointed to the Ballistics Branch of the Army Weapons Department as assistant to Captain von Horstig. This branch, to which problems of rocket development had been transferred in 1929, was confronted at first by a muddle difficult to straighten out. Neither industry nor the technical colleges were paying any attention to the development of high-powered rocket propulsion. There were only individual inventors who played about without financial support, assisted by more or less able collaborators. They were forced to resort to publicity demonstrations and to write exaggerated newspaper articles to earn a living. This behavior naturally led to opposition by college professors and accredited scientists. Moreover, each individual inventor maintained a feud with everyone else who took an interest in rockets. Until 1932 no solid scientific research or development work was done in this field in Germany. It was not, for instance, possible before the middle of 1932 to obtain from the Raketen-flugplatz [1] in Berlin any sort of records showing performance and fuel consumption during experiments.

The Army Weapons Department was forced to get in touch with the individual inventors, support them financially, and await results. For two years the department tried in vain to obtain something to go on. No progress was being made in the work. There was also the danger that thoughtless chatter might result in the department's becoming known as the financial backer of rocket development. We had therefore to take other steps.

As we did not succeed in interesting heavy industry there was nothing left to do but to set up our own experimental station for liquid-propellant rockets at the department's proving ground in Kummersdorf near Berlin. We wanted to have done once and for all with theory, unproved claims, and boastful fantasy, and to arrive at conclusions based on a sound scientific foundation. We were tired of imaginative projects concerning space travel. The

[1] This was the name of the proving ground of the Society for Space Travel (VfR) in a northern suburb of Berlin.

value of the sixth decimal place in the calculation of a trajectory to Venus interested us as little as the problem of heating and air regeneration in the pressurized cabin of a Mars ship. We wanted to advance the practice of rocket building with scientific thoroughness. We wanted thrust-time curves of the performance of rocket motors. We wanted to know what fuel consumption per second we had to allow for, what fuel mixture would be best, how to deal with the temperatures occurring in the process, what types of injection, combustion-chamber shape, and exhaust nozzle would yield the best performance. We intended to establish the fundamentals, create the necessary tools, and study the basic conditions. First and foremost came the propulsion unit.

It was not easy at first to get my young collaborators away from their space dreams and make them settle down quietly to hard research and development work. We began with the development of a rocket motor with a thrust of 650 pounds. We meant to bring this motor to a high level of performance, to gather experience, tabulate laws and principles, and so create a basis for further construction.

The mistakes we made then may, of course, cause smiles now, but we trod with the fine freedom of ignorance in a new field of technology and learned from failure and bitter experience.

I shall never be tempted into argument about who got the right ideas first. Let those who have the time, energy, and money fight out claims to priority. I think it probable that any genuine inventor, research worker, or engineer who had the problem to deal with under identical conditions and worked painstakingly along scientific lines would have achieved practically the same results. The time was ripe and the basic conditions were present.

Man's technical progress does not come only from men with great ideas, but almost as frequently from those who first apply unshakable faith and tireless energy to an idea's materialization. The history of technology teaches us that all who venture thus have to struggle against doubt, mistrust, and mockery. Yet in the hour of success hundreds and thousands come forward, bent on proving that the idea was stolen, the achievement due to the earlier labors of others.

There is no point in arguing with such people. They will never understand how much serious, painstaking toil is necessary before initial success can be registered. They will be equally unable to see that in technology the first practical realization of an idea must always be faulty, that one has always to start at the beginning, at some small fixed point from which one can go on. The finished article of modern technology is never the first-fruit of a single individual or a small group of people. It is always the product of years of intensive work by a succession of outstanding scientists, engineers, and technicians.

In my view the immortal services rendered by the great men of technology lie in their having given their successors a first practical demonstration of the existence of new paths and new fields of endeavor. One ought never to forget, for instance, when one looks at a modern Diesel engine developing thousands of horsepower, what hard work and faith were needed to enable the original Diesel engine to achieve its first working rhythm at Augsburg.

One might say that in the history of technology there have been only three really great inventions which have decisively influenced, or will so influence, the history of mankind for thousands of years. These are the wheel, with which man conquered the earth; the screw, with which they conquered the seas and the air; and now, at the start of a new era in human history, rocket propulsion, which will help men to conquer space and push forward to the stars.

The early years of our activity shine in my memory with imperishable luster. They were years of groping toward creation, of the delight of success, of progressive work in common among inseparable companions. But they were also years of dark and desperate hours of defeat and of unending battle against human stupidity and lack of faith.

CHAPTER 3

THE FIRST STEP: EXPERIMENTAL STATION KUMMERSDORF WEST

The Experimental Station West was situated between the two Kummersdorf firing ranges, about 17 miles south of Berlin, in a clearing in the open pine forest of the province of Brandenburg. To the already existing test stand for powder rockets we added the first two buildings for the new venture and then the first test stand ever established in Germany for liquid-propellant rocket development, which was fully equipped with all available resources of measurement technique. We improvised offices, a designing room, measurement rooms, darkrooms, and a tiny workshop. We drew up our first schedule of work in discussions that lasted for hours. In the months that followed everyone was bent over a drawing board or busy at a lathe. There were delays from week to week and from day to day, but at last we were ready. The first firing test could take place.

The cold bit through the thick soles of my riding boots. It crept up my body until I felt miserably frozen in my short fur jacket. It was a frosty clear night, that twenty-first of December, 1932. I had snuggled up close to a fir tree. Whenever I showed any sign of abandoning my position I was brought up short by a shout of "Keep under cover! Ignition any moment now!"

"Cover" was an optimistic term. It could hardly be expected that the slender fir trunk 4 inches thick would provide much protection against an explosion. I was standing 10 yards away from our first test stand. We were very proud of that test stand, finished only a few days before. Three concrete walls, 18 feet long and 12 feet high, were arranged in the form of a U, the place of a fourth wall being taken by folding metal doors. There was a sliding wooden roof covered with tarpaper, which could be moved on rollers by means of a small winch.

When doors and roof were both closed the effect was of a big weatherproof testing room. In the back wall were a number of holes leading to an observation or measurement chamber. This mysterious room contained an incredible chaos of blue, red, green, and yellow pipes for measuring, feeding, and testing propellants and high-pressure nitrogen, in addition to valves, meters, and recording apparatus. This apparent confusion was at first bewildering. The experts of course considered it all very simple.

At the corners of the back wall there were two openings at eye level, fitted with mirrors to enable the testing staff to observe the rocket motor. In the middle of the same wall were two iron handwheels, their shafts leading through the wall to valves. The place was full of switches, little valve handwheels, reducing valves, three-way cocks, electrical instruments, clocks, and rows of meters and other gadgets connected with the fuel tanks and to critical points of the combustion chamber that needed careful watching.

We sought data on flow rates, pressures, and so forth, throughout the system, in the tanks, pipe conduits, cooling jackets, and at many points in the combustion chamber, for we had to ascertain temperatures and gradients to discover the best fuel-mixture ratio and to measure thrust performance.

The green, high-pressure steel flasks for nitrogen stood chained to the side wall. Powerful electric lamps filled the narrow room, only 12 feet long, with dazzling light. Beneath two side tables a pair of electric radiators distributed cozy warmth.

The roof above the test stand was pushed back, the doors were wide open. In the dazzling glare of two searchlights I could see the test frame in the middle of the testing room, with the pear-shaped, silver-gray rocket motor, made of duraluminum, about 20 inches long. It was mounted vertically with the exhaust nozzle downward. Around the chamber were arranged four tubes. These would convey the power of the exhaust blast to a spring connected by

thin steel wires running on rollers to a thrust-measuring instrument in the observation room. The combustion chamber, with its
round head and tapering exhaust nozzle, was calculated to develop
a thrust of 650 pounds.

On the right-hand side of the measuring room a big, spherical,
ice-covered aluminum container with liquid oxygen was suspended
from springs. The connecting pipes leading to the rocket motor
were frosted too. Ice mist rose from them. A similar container for
75-per-cent ethyl alcohol hung on the left-hand side. The alcohol
conduit forked into two branches, each connected to the bulbous
edge of the exhaust nozzle. Thin piano wires from the tanks led
over rollers through the concrete wall to instruments that would
trace the graphs of fuel consumption during firing.

The rocket motor itself had double walls. Between them rose
cooling alcohol at a high rate of flow from bottom to top. The
alcohol, warmed to 158 degrees Fahrenheit, entered the inner
chamber through small sievelike injection nozzles in the chamber
head. It was met there by liquid oxygen ejected from a centrally
placed brass sprayer, shaped like an inverted mushroom and
perforated with many small holes. These jets, with an injection
pressure of several atmospheres, collided with great force, were
atomized and mixed, to increase the rapidity of combustion.

Under the nozzle a black opening yawned in the iron-plated
floor to receive the blast. A blast deflector lined with firebricks
would split the jet and divert it right and left at an angle of 90
degrees through brick-lined channels into two tall vertical shafts
at the outer wall of the building, and so to the open air.

In the control room the engineer, Walter Riedel, stood on a
narrow wooden grating, grasping two big steering wheels. When
pressure was right in the spherical containers a turn of the wheels
would open the two main valves and let the propellants into the
combustion chamber. Riedel's eyes were on the meters. Beside him
the mechanic Grünow was regulating the flow of nitrogen from
the pressure flasks into the tanks by handwheels controlling the
reducing valves. He kept his eyes fixed on the quivering needles
of the gauges showing tank pressures.

At the main door of the test stand, von Braun, very cold, was stamping his feet. He was holding a rod 12 feet long with a can of gasoline fastened to the end. Riedel called out from behind the wall that pressure was now correct, and von Braun lit his gigantic match and held the flame under the exhaust nozzle.

Suddenly a round white cloud appeared under the exhaust nozzle and sank slowly to the ground. A clear liquid, alcohol, came trickling after it. Riedel opened the valves and von Braun moved his rod to bring the flame into contact with the fumes.

There was a swoosh, a hiss, and—crash!

Clouds of smoke rose. A single flame darted briefly upward and vanished. Cables, boards, metal sheeting, fragments of steel and aluminum flew whistling through the air. The searchlights went out.

Silence.

In the suddenly darkened pit of the testing room a milky, slimy mixture of alcohol and oxygen burned spasmodically with flames of different shapes and sizes, occasionally crackling and detonating like fireworks. Steam hissed. Cables were on fire in a hundred places. Thick, black, stinging fumes of burning rubber filled the air. Von Braun and I stared at each other wide-eyed. We were uninjured.

The test stand had been wrecked. Steel girders and pillars were bent and twisted. The metal doors had been torn off their hinges. Immediately above our heads sharp, jagged splinters of steel were stuck in the brown bark of the trees. Riedel and Grünow came running up, agitated and full of concern. Then we had to laugh. What fools we had been! How could we ever have made such an elementary mistake? We understood now. Alas, that winter's night of 1932 we could not foresee how many more fundamental errors we were to fall into before success gradually rewarded our efforts many years later.

Our nineteen-year-old "student," Wernher von Braun, had come to us fresh from his work on the Raketenflugplatz in Berlin Reinickendorf. That enterprise was slowly dying of chronic lack of money, so he had joined the Army Weapons Department on October 1, 1932. He now belonged to my specialist staff.

I had been struck during my casual visits to Reinickendorf by the energy and shrewdness with which this tall, fair, young student with the broad massive chin went to work, and by his astonishing theoretical knowledge. It had seemed to me that he grasped the problems and that his chief concern was to lay bare the difficulties. In this respect he had been a refreshing change from most of the leading men at the place. When General Becker later decided to approve our Army establishment for liquid-propellant rockets, I had put Wernher von Braun first on my list of proposed technical assistants.

He had taken up astronomy as a hobby in his boarding-school days on one of the Frisian islands. When he went on to the Berlin Institute of Technology he soon found a way of attaching himself to the Raketenflugplatz. In the work going on there he believed he could see a remote possibility that one day he might reach his beloved stars. In his free time, or rather when he cut lectures, he worked as an assistant, as a designer, as a theoretician, and finally even as a member of the board. He came of aristocratic old German stock and his scientific bent had at first aroused the disapproval of his family, with their centuries-old tradition of land-ownership. When his father came to see us at Kummersdorf in 1933 he told me with frequent headshakings that he had no idea where his son had acquired this strange technological bent.

Our first assistant, most enthusiastic and able, was the mechanic Heinrich Grünow. And on November 1, 1932, I had succeeded in obtaining a third man, Walter Riedel, an engineer from the Heyland Works at Brietz near Berlin. In association with that firm in 1929 and 1930, Max Valier had been one of the first to experiment with a liquid-propellant rocket motor, which he used to drive a small racing car. Valier had met a pioneer's death there on May 17, 1930.

Riedel's position was that of test engineer and designer. He was a short, sedate man with a permanently dignified and serious expression and a somewhat phlegmatic temperament. He was a most versatile practical engineer, with the special asset of being experienced in handling liquid oxygen. He seemed to me to provide the right counterpoise to the rather temperamental—and at that time self-taught—technician, von Braun. Riedel with his calm, deliberate mind, deep knowledge, and practical experience repeatedly managed to guide the bubbling stream of von Braun's ideas into steadier channels. He took von Braun under his wing and equipped him with the technique required for the work.

Three weeks after the first unlucky experiment just described, our first rocket motor was burning at the test stand, now rebuilt. Unfortunately it burned in the literal sense of the word. It had been working flawlessly for a few seconds when a dazzling white light appeared in the bluish-red gas jet, indicating a surplus of oxygen. The light grew brighter and brighter. Aluminum was on fire. The chamber burned right through. Thus we encountered our first cooling problem.

New chambers and new injection nozzles were designed and welded together in the tiny workshop. For some weeks all went well and we made progress. Then we had setbacks again. No motor seemed to stand up any more. The pendulum swung from success to the most dismal failure, from desperation to optimism. After months of work we hit on a form of 650-pound-thrust chamber that gave consistent performance. But it was still a very bad one. It had an exhaust velocity of 5570 feet per second. We measured the flame temperature, took samples of the gas jet, analyzed the gases, changed the mixture ratio, and still couldn't get more than 5900 to 6200 feet per second. We then tried different propellants.

In 1931 we had given Heyland's an order to develop a small liquid-propellant rocket motor for our basic experiments. It had a thrust of 45 pounds, was double-walled for cooling, cylindrical in shape, and made of steel. It was now handed over to the Research Branch of the Army Weapons Department for basic research and experiments with different propellant mixtures. Dr. Wahmke, in charge of experimental work, Voellmecke, chief

pyrotechnician, and some students from the Research Branch conducted these tests in a small test stand hastily improvised near
the old one out of boards and planks sheathed with armor plate.

Dr. Wahmke was then experimenting with 90 per cent hydrogen
peroxide and alcohol. Neither of these two fuels was dangerous
by itself if properly handled. At a fateful moment one March
evening in 1934 Dr. Wahmke decided to mix the two fuels in a
steel tank, feed them into the rocket chamber through a single
valve, and then ignite. He was well aware of the risk he was
taking; no safeguards had been installed in the pipe leading from
the tank suspended just above the motor. He was obsessed with
the idea of finding out whether there was any danger in using
propellants already mixed before combustion. He telephoned the
mess, where he knew people would still be about long after
working hours, and asked that help should be sent if there were
an explosion. Then he told his colleagues to leave the stand. They
refused to do so, and all smoked cigarettes. At last they fired the
chamber.

The little ignition explosion in the chamber ran through the
conduit to the tank. When help came a few minutes later, nothing
was left of the test stand except the lead pipe of the water supply.
Of the four who had shared the experiment, three were dead, including Dr. Wahmke. They were the first but also the last to
give their lives in the course of rocket development under the
Army Weapons Department.

In those first years, in addition to the department, an immense
number of individual inventors were busy on rocket problems.
Most of them came to us and offered us their ideas. It was our
job to separate the wheat from the chaff, and that was no small
task in a sphere of activity so beset with humbugs, charlatans, and
scientific cranks, and so sparsely populated with men of real
ability.

An engineer named Pietsch, formerly employed at the Heyland
Works, offered the Army Weapons Department a fully automatic
liquid-propellant motor with a thrust of 650 pounds and a burning
period of 60 seconds. We checked his proposal and found it prac-

ticable. He was given advances for materials and received repeated subsidies. One day he disappeared, leaving behind a colleague, one Arthur Rudolph, a lean, starved-looking engineer with
reddish-blond hair. Rudolph turned out to be the real inventor of
the motor. We invested more money in the affair and helped him
with our own facilities, and after a few weeks he demonstrated his
motor to us at Kummersdorf. It was made entirely of copper, with
the oxygen tank above and the alcohol tank, enclosing and cooling
the combustion chamber, below. The tanks were spherical in shape.
The specifications were met. We found we could use Rudolph and
took him into our organization, where he became one of our top
experts.

Sensational newspaper reports and letters of recommendation
drew our attention to a so-called engineer named Wilhelm Belz,
who was supposed to have made a liquid-propellant rocket and
fired it to a great but unspecified range. Autographed picture
postcards showed him standing beside his tall silver-gray rocket.
The picture was impressive, but closer investigation proved that
the man knew nothing whatever about liquid-propellant rockets. He had been leading a large following of "experts" up the
garden for months on end by means of an ordinary blackpowder
rocket built into a gigantic dummy of sheet metal.

A man named Albert Püllenberg was working at Hanover in the
most miserable circumstances, with an enthusiasm exceeded only
by his lack of resources. A short visit to him convinced me that
he would never get any further by the road he was taking. I suggested that he should first take his engineer's degree, and later
on, when he had absorbed the full meaning of Schiller's advice,
"If you cannot be a whole body, join such a whole as a serving
limb," he should come and see me. Years later he appeared and
joined us.

We had created at Kummersdorf the best testing equipment and
testing methods for both solid- and liquid-propellant rockets. Inventors who traded on the presumed ignorance of the department
and the difficulty of investigating their claims, and made exaggerated and fantastic ones, were quickly exposed. But from among

the many who came to us with rocket ideas, we did get some outstanding men.

The work went on. We designed all sorts of injection systems
and tried them out, without any improvement in performance.
The ratio between fuel consumption and thrust was not changed
either. But at least we managed to avoid burning out the chamber
and setting the injection nozzles on fire, and we could now carry
out as many as three or four test firings of the same motor, obtaining uniform performance each time.

Thus after a very hard year's work we had laid a frail foundation on which we could build. Our need now was for higher
authority to give our work due recognition and to provide us
with money—a great deal of money—and with the staff for carrying on. But first of all we had to provide conclusive evidence that
a liquid-propellant rocket could hold to its prescribed trajectory.

Only now did we begin to give any serious consideration to all
the problems involved in making our projectile fly. We had experience with powder rockets only. We knew the difficulties of
stabilization, how such a projectile could be affected by wind,
angle of launching, the shift of the center of gravity as the propellant was consumed, and other adverse factors. However, we
finally decided to plan the first complete missile, Aggregate 1
(A-1).

We aimed at a high-speed rocket. We did not intend, as the
Berlin Raketenflugplatz had, to build a nose-drive rocket; in
other words, to put the motor in front so that the exhaust surrounded and warmed the fuel tanks mounted behind. Our 650-
pound-thrust motor either would have burst the tanks in a few
seconds or else would have had to be mounted too far forward
for any kind of stability. Air resistance, too, would have been considerably higher.

I remember the great disappointment in August 1932, during
a demonstration at Kummersdorf, when a rocket of this type built
by the Raketenflugplatz group, after rising vertically for 100-odd
feet, sharply swerved into a horizontal course and crashed in a
nearby forest. This 12-foot "one-stick repulsor" had a diameter of

4 inches and carried at the extreme front end an aluminum rocket motor within an egg-shaped, water-filled cooling jacket. The thrust was about 130 pounds and the exhaust was directed at a sheet-metal cone which was welded to the top end of the oxygen tank and which was supposed to prevent the exhaust from touching the tank walls. Two curved thin pipes, carrying oxygen and alcohol respectively, held the rocket motor at the desired distance from the tanks and also served to transmit the pull of the burning motor to the body of the rocket. The two tanks were placed one behind the other and were connected by a piece of pipe providing enough empty space for two manometers. Through holes in the connecting pipe it was possible to read the tank pressures. Standpipes conducted the two liquids to the top of the rocket. The oxygen tank was pressurized when the valves were closed by the pressure of evaporation, while the alcohol was fed by compressed nitrogen. A container at the end of this rod-shaped rocket held a parachute and flare. Four small stabilizing fins of aluminum were welded to the stern. The rocket had a take-off weight of about 45 pounds and a deadweight of some 22 pounds. Exhaust velocity was claimed to be over 6500 feet per second but was certainly not more than 5600 feet per second in reality.

The failure of this demonstration brought home to us in the Army Weapons Department how many scientific and technical questions needed answering before we could hope to construct a rocket that could fly efficiently. We had still paid far too little attention to the problem of stability and control. We were still too much influenced by the traditional ways of thinking expressed in the ballistic reports of the department. We were still unable to shake ourselves quite free of the idea that what was valid for shells must also be valid for rockets.

Our notion was that the rocket should achieve stability by rotation about its axis of length. But how to realize such an idea? The rocket would have to rotate but not the fuel tanks. Fuel would rise up the walls of the tanks as a result of centrifugal force, and this would make feeding of the propellants difficult.

I suggested that we confine rotation to a heavy steel section, serving as the payload container, and with its axis running on ball bearings, thus constituting a kind of gyroscope and giving stability to the rocket.

We designed the A-1. The rotating section, weighing 85 pounds, was placed at the nose of the missile, which was about 4.6 feet long and 1 foot in diameter. Approximately 85 pounds of propellants were to be forced by nitrogen pressure from the tanks into the combustion chamber, which developed a thrust of some 650 pounds and was built into the fuel tank at the rear of the rocket. The rotating section, made to form the rotor of a three-phase current motor, was to be brought up to its highest speed before launching. The A-1 would be fired vertically from a launching rack several yards high. With a take-off weight of about 330 pounds, initial acceleration would be practically equal to the ordinary acceleration due to gravity at the earth's surface—that is, to 1 g.

The motor was constructed and, after breaking down a few times, worked perfectly. But before the outward shape of the A-1 was finished we decided to go on at once to the next stage in the development of the rocket motor. Shortly afterward we had ready the first design for a new motor, made of duraluminum, with a thrust of 2200 pounds. We meant to build bigger rockets. It was important to find out whether our experience so far was valid for them too.

Our one and only test stand was by now inadequate. It was fully occupied with trials of the 650-pound motor. In 1934 we therefore built a new test stand for high-performance motors, incorporating the results of our experience to date. Already we were planning a third stand for tests with complete rockets.

We toiled on and on and were repeatedly delayed by setbacks. We came to recognize that small-scale experimental data did not automatically apply to a big chamber as well as to a small one. Again and again the motor burned through at the most dangerous points: the throat of the nozzle, the transition from the cylindrical part of the chamber to the nozzle, the head of the chamber, and the injection nozzles. Moreover, we had decided to give a new

rocket a burning time of 45 seconds instead of the 16 seconds the
A-1 had. New cooling problems arose. Months went by and we
made no progress.

At the same time we were busy with a whole series of other important problems, for instance, stabilizing the bigger rockets. Von
Braun got in touch with the Kreiselgeräte G.m.b.H. (Gyroscope
Company) at Brietz near Berlin. One of their directors was a
former Austrian naval officer named Boykow, a tall, robust man
with bright eyes in a shrewd face dominated by a tremendous
nose. He was the leading spirit of the firm, an expert full of ideas
and far ahead of his time in all questions relating to gyroscopes.

When von Braun told Boykow what he wanted Boykow answered with a smile, "I've been expecting a call like yours for
many years and I've prepared for it."

It turned out that in addition to thinking about it he had already made some sample and detail models. An intimate exchange
of ideas followed. This clear-thinking scientist and practical man
was the best help we could have dreamed of. We learned that the
point was not merely to correct deflections of the rocket's axis
from that of the gyroscope but to check the tendency to deflection as it arose. Only if we initiated an immediate counter-
movement could we prevent a divergent trend in the oscillations.
Stabilization equipment would have to be sensitive to acceleration.
We thus gradually came to see realized our vague hope of stabilizing fair-sized rockets during the firing period with a gyroscope
system working on three axes.

The external shape of the big rocket was still quite undeter-
mined. It was clear to us that it must have "arrow stability"; in
other words, the center of gravity must be situated in front of
the theoretical center of pressure of all the aerodynamic forces
operating. In order to shift this point back, the missile would have
to be provided with tail fins. According to the standard text-
book *Ballistics,* by Professor Cranz, relating to projectile ballistics,
experience had proved that it was impossible for bodies with arrow stability to accomplish perfect flight at supersonic speeds. But

supersonic speed was needed to obtain access to space. Nor was that all. We had to be prepared to go up the whole scale of speed, from zero to many times sonic velocity, with a projectile stable throughout.

Our problem was to find such a configuration. No excessive air drag must take place and no excessive control forces must be required. We knew that it would be a long and difficult business and that a wind tunnel would be needed for it.

The next great question was automatic stabilization. Were we to use air rudders operated by servomechanisms? It would be impossible to do so at the beginning of the trajectory, for at the low take-off velocity the aerodynamic forces on the rudders would be negligible. Afterward the steady velocity increase would cause a steady change of the forces. This had to be taken into account. The power required for steering would therefore have to be varied constantly to suit changing speeds—a serious complication.

We considered mounting the motor in gymbals, thereby obtaining the required control. It was theoretically feasible, but the motor would then have to be placed behind the tanks, and this would make the missile too long. Our motors were still very long. For our next project we provided, as before, for the motor to be placed inside the alcohol tank.

We might have developed four small steering motors arranged in the form of a cross and so steered big rockets even in empty space, but that too seemed too bold an initial step. The solution of this difficulty was a simple one that came quite of its own accord. The exhaust speed of the combustion gases was practically unchanged during the whole period of burning. Could not the control vanes be inside the gas jet? Was there any material which would resist exhaust-flame temperature throughout the burning period and which possessed such high thermal resistance that it would not melt, like butter in the sun, at an exhaust velocity of almost 6500 feet per second?

We might well have been daunted by the multiplicity of the tasks before us. Luckily the difficulties were for the most part still

entirely unknown to us. We attacked our problems with the
courage of inexperience and had no thought of the time it might
take us to solve them.

We believed that with the A-1 we had completed the first of
our tasks. After various checks and tests, however, we found that
the A-1 was too nose-heavy. The center of gravity lay too far
ahead of the center of pressure. The A-1 could not therefore be
wholly reliable in flight.

We got out a new design. The result was the A-2. So far as the
motor was concerned, it was a replica of the A-1, but the gyroscope had been moved from the nose of the missile to the middle,
between the oxygen and alcohol tanks.

By October 1, 1934, the static tests and assembly were completed. On that date I had to take over the last brief military
command I ever held, a battery at Königsbrück, training with
the first powder-rocket launchers, in the construction and development of which I had taken a leading part. I had no idea then that
these same powder rockets would acquire such great importance
a few years later on the battlefields of Russia, France, Norway,
and North Africa. Much less did I suspect that on their appearance
at the front at the beginning of the Russian campaign in June
1941 they would usher in their own new era.

My last day at Kummersdorf was given to a detailed discussion
of the rocket A-2—"4.5 calibers long," as it was called in accordance with artillery tradition. At the beginning of December 1934,
the first two A-2 liquid-propellant rockets developed by the Army
were successfully fired from the island of Borkum in the North
Sea. The maximum altitude reached was 1.4 miles.

We had made a beginning.

CHAPTER 4

"HOW MUCH DO YOU WANT?"

We had to do battle constantly, though there was no war on. It was a good thing we had no idea then what forces we should be up against as development proceeded. In comparison with what came later these early disputes were child's play.

When Professor Becker was still a colonel and head of the Ballistics and Munitions Division he had at first allocated a small sum from the funds of his branches for our rocket work. On becoming chief of the whole Development Section of the Army Weapons Department he directed the various divisions of the Development Section to transfer a small percentage of their funds to us. But one mustn't imagine that we now had money, material, and personnel in unlimited quantities. On the contrary, the Bureau of the Budget kept a keen and jaundiced eye on us. We were not permitted to order either machine tools or office equipment. Only test facilities and apparatus pertaining thereto could be bought.

However, we were young, and inventive in more ways than one. We soon found means of defeating bureaucratic red tape. We learned in a hard school how to get everything we wanted. We acquired things "as per sample." For instance, even the keenest Budget Bureau official could not suspect that "Appliance for milling wooden dowels up to 10 millimeters in diameter, as per sample" meant a pencil sharpener, or that "Instrument for recording test data with rotating roller as per sample" meant a typewriter. The whole secret was circumlocution. And if there was nothing else to do, we entrenched ourselves behind the magic word "secret." There the Budget Bureau was powerless.

Once, in the summer of 1933, we bought two boxes of Christmas tree sparklers. The idea was to use these sparklers inside the nozzle for igniting the first drops of oxygen and alcohol. A year passed. Then the Bureau of the Budget asked what Christmas sparklers were used for in the middle of summer. We replied tersely, "For experiments." But the Bureau of the Budget was not happy with this answer, and eight weeks later asked us what kind of experiments. We answered, "Secret experiments." Then they gave up.

In December 1934 we had our first success in firing liquid-propellant rockets. As development work progressed, our need for money and technical experts increased, and we were compelled again and again to bring ourselves to the attention of ever higher authority. We had big desires. Our area at Kummersdorf had long since become too small for us. Even at the firing of our powder rockets we never felt quite at ease, for there was always the danger, particularly in those early stages, that our flaming messengers might follow their own unpredictable paths, and this risk was still greater with liquid-propellant rockets. We needed a new experimental site. We wanted to build—to build on the grand scale, and beautifully. We had no desire to see our new factories, planned to cover every phase of development, put up in the style of "Unit Model 78, Old Type" by the Army Construction Section. The severe beauty of the new Air Force buildings had bewitched both ourselves and the architects we employed. But where on earth were we to build? And where was the money to come from?

Again and again we tried the old dodge that nearly always works in matters of weapon development—demonstrating our wares in front of the prominent people who sit on the money bags.

In March 1936 we managed to persuade General von Fritsch to visit our experimental station at Kummersdorf. After a few short but thorough lectures, illustrated with colored drawings and many diagrams, we demonstrated our three thunderous rocket motors, with their 650-pound, 2200-pound, and 3500-pound-thrust. Hardly had the echo of the motors died away in the pine woods than the General assured us of his full support, provided we used the funds to turn our rocket drive into a serviceable weapon of war. Bluntly and dispassionately he put the all-important question, "How much do you want?"

This question always made us feel uncomfortable. We needed an impossible sum running into seven figures, for we had had a new idea which would not leave us. We wanted to investigate and develop on a single site everything that seemed essential to the effective employment of such a new and powerful weapon. We wanted to develop, not only the rocket itself, but also the necessary ground handling and testing equipment, and to study all its implications in the most diverse branches of technology and science. We wanted to start with applied research and end up with a fully developed article ready for production in the factories. In short, we wished to put through on our own account a complete program. We needed a research and development site fully equipped with all the latest resources of science and technology. And that cost money.

General von Fritsch's visit led to orders that enabled us to request funds directly for our branch from then on. Soon after that we succeeded in interesting the chief of the Development Division of the Air Ministry, Lieutenant Colonel von Richthofen. We described to him in glowing terms the possibilities of using rocket motors as take-off help for heavy bombers and of equiping fighter aircraft with rocket power plants, and suggested building a combined establishment. Richthofen agreed and put in a report to General Kesselring, chief of Aircraft Construction.

Finally, in April 1936, the highly important but also critical conference with General Kesselring took place. With the aid of maps, plans, and diagrams, General Becker, von Braun, Lieutenant Colonel von Richthofen, and I explained the first draft scheme for an "Army Experimental Station" at Peenemünde. Kesselring could not help smiling at our enthusiastic and even dramatic picture of the future, but at last he gave his approval. He agreed to our proposal that his own construction department should build the station at Peenemünde. There was to be an Air Force and Army division under unified administration by the Army. The Air

Force and the Army were to share expenses. When the construction work was finished the whole area would be transferred to Army control.

A remote place for our experiments had now become necessary also for reasons of secrecy. The characteristic roar of our motors must sound only in utter isolation. It would not do to have to wait until summer holiday makers had gone to make our test launchings from the seashore. We must be able to work independently of season and environment. For reasons of safety we had to fire out to sea and to observe the entire trajectory from land.

Wernher von Braun had been busy looking for such a place ever since the middle of December 1935. He thought he had found a suitable spot near Binz on the island of Rügen, but it turned out that the German Labor Front had already taken possession of that coast as a "Strength through Joy" recreation center. During the Christmas holidays, which von Braun spent with relatives near Anklam, his attention was drawn to Peenemünde. He found that the extensive forest area in the north of the island of Usedom was suitable for our purpose.

When I visited the area a few days later the Peenemünde project began to take shape. The place was far away from any large towns or traffic of any kind, and consisted of dunes and marshland overgrown with ancient oaks and pines, nestling in untroubled solitude behind a reedy foreland reaching far out into smooth water. Big Pomeranian deer with dark antlers roamed through the heather and among the bilberry bushes of the woods right to the sands of the low-lying coast. Swarms of ducks, crested grebes, coots, and swans inhabited this beautiful spot, undisturbed for years by the report of the huntsman's shotgun. The bustle of the seashore resorts strung along the coast like a necklace of pearls never invaded the lonely inlet of Peenemünde.

I thought there would be no difficulty in building a railway and roads and concealing the really important installations in the woods. As against Rügen, we had an immeasurable advantage: a small island which faced the Peene estuary, the Greifswalder Oie. There we could carry out our experiments unnoticed throughout the year. We had a range of over 250 miles eastward along the Pomeranian coast.

We still had only a small budget and staff; we did not yet know what our big rocket was eventually to look like or what other tasks were in store for us. To avoid being disturbed by further building for some time we had to plan the laboratories, workshops, and test stands so that they would need no additions for a number of years.

When Kesselring agreed in a conference that the Air Ministry would pay half the cost of the project there seemed to be a good prospect that our far-reaching plans would mature. What amazed us was the speed at which they became reality. High authority virtually suffered from an attack of acute generosity. On the very evening of the conference a senior official of the Air Ministry telephoned to tell us that the land had been purchased for 750,000 marks. He had been immediately sent to Wolgast in a high-powered car to buy the desired area from the city, which owned it.

Here was action indeed!

CHAPTER 5

THE GREIFSWALDER OIE

At the beginning of December 1937 we fired our first shots from the Greifswalder Oie. This small, narrow island, north of the island of Usedom, had been like a swarming antheap for several weeks beforehand. The Greifswalder Oie is 1100 yards long and about 300 broad at its widest point. It lies 5 miles from the northern coast of Usedom and 7½ miles from Rügen. The steep, loamy coast, lashed by storm and surf in winter, rises to a height of about 60 feet above the level of the Baltic. A tiny fishing harbor on the southwest coast is connected with the uplands by a narrow sandy road. The southern part of the island, containing an inn and a few houses, was where we lived. Through the center of the island, as far as the lighthouse on the northern point, runs a rough country road. One Herr Halliger, owner of the inn and leasee of the island, attended with inexhaustible good humor to our bodily needs and to the warmth of the outer and inner man, a matter of dire necessity at this cold season of the year.

That spring the tranquillity of the islet had been interrupted. One day a number of small motor launches filled with building personnel and surveyors had arrived in the little harbor. Next came a large vessel of unusual appearance, such as had never been seen before in that part of the Baltic. She carried building materials and equipment. Halliger recollected that he had come across that antediluvian craft once before, in Stralsund. She had been a car and passenger ferry then. A typical example of mid-nineteenth-century shipbuilding, she possessed large cabins with decrepit furniture upholstered in red plush, a quantity of gleaming brass fittings and mountings, towering upper works, and a high funnel. As she was further distinguished by shallow draught and extensive cargo space, she was now serving as our transport from the mainland to the Oie.

The next to arrive were the harbor dredgers and barges. A bustle now began with which the island was wholly unfamiliar. The harbor was dredged. Berths and landing facilities had to be created for big vessels and heavy cargoes. The cart-track to the uplands was given a firm surface of planks. In front of the storm-tossed coppice that stood to the east of the track a square concrete platform went up. A pit was excavated opposite it, at the edge of the forest, and a dugout was built.

The builders and builders' laborers departed. Engineers and craftsmen took their place. Then came more builders. Lines and cable after cable were laid between the shelter and the central point of the platform. Dugout, lighthouse, and inn were connected by telephone. The dugout was transformed into an observation post with look-out slits and gauges of all descriptions on the walls. Thin copper piping was fitted. The builders put up four small concrete pyramids to take the phototheodolites. The pyramids were given wooden platforms and in the coppice immediately behind the shelter two big open clearings were made and leveled off.

The builders left and were replaced by a fresh wave of busy people. They brought with them a gigantic tent which they set up in one of the clearings in the coppice. In the other they erected a wooden shed for the storage of Diesel oil and alcohol. Generators were unloaded at the harbor and brought to the coppice. Wiring was laid for electric light. Gasoline, materials, and tools arrived by sea.

Weeks passed in a whirl of activity.

One day at the end of November the ferryboat delivered two large boxes painted dark gray. They were 23 feet long and 4¾ feet in height and breadth. These giants' coffins were unloaded with great care and cautiously conveyed by truck to the tent. There they were guarded night and day. Shortly afterward two

pressure, and a radio receiver which would cut off burning on an emergency signal from the ground if the rocket broke away from its course.

Beneath the instrument compartment was the oxygen tank, and beneath this the propellant tank, containing the built-in rocket motor of duraluminum, some 6 feet long. The liquid-nitrogen reservoir was built into the oxygen tank and fitted with an immersion heater for pressurizing the tanks. The parachute container was between the two tanks. The parachute would be automatically ejected at the greatest altitude reached—that is, when the rocket, ready to fall back, assumed an exactly horizontal position. At an angle of 30 degrees, propulsion would be automatically cut off.

The light-alloy tanks, with a capacity of 1000 pounds, had such strong walls that they could withstand feed pressures up to 294 pounds per square inch. The take-off weight was 1650 pounds. For a period of 45 seconds the motor would develop a thrust of 1.5 tons with an exhaust velocity of about 6200 feet per second. Around the bottom ends of the four long, slender fins, which projected outward about 8 inches, was a plastic ring some 10 inches wide, to prevent the fins from fluttering and to promote stable flight. The copper-wire coils of the aerial controlling the emergency cut-off were built into this ring. The four fins stood firmly on the plastic bearing plates of the firing table, which could be rotated. The table was provided with rows of plugs for connecting the measurements and observation shelter with the rocket, and for supplying electric current through the fins, as well as for transmitting measurement data from steering components and valves. When the rocket rose, these contacts would be broken and the rocket would go on its way in fully automatic fashion.

As I waited for our first firing from the Greifswalder Oie my thoughts went back over the long road from the inception of the Peenemünde Army Experimental Station to the present first launching. We had been so delighted when we heard that Peenemünde had been purchased! It meant we had taken the big stride from straitened means and small operations to really large-scale planning and thus to success.

A few days after General von Fritsch's visit in March 1936, I had sat with von Braun and Walter Riedel at Kummersdorf, studying plans for the Peenemünde project. We had discussed the layout of test stands on the east coast. At that time we had also conceived the plan of setting up a test stand in the north of the area for really big motors and complete rocket assemblies.

The A-3 rocket we were then developing had not been equipped to take any payload. It was a purely experimental missile. As we kept on pestering the Army chiefs for money for continued development we were told we should get it only for rockets that would be capable of throwing big loads over long ranges with a good prospect of hitting the target. In our youthful zeal we promised all that was asked, never suspecting what difficulties would arise in consequence.

We discussed what size of motor the test stand should be designed for. Von Braun and Riedel were already thinking of a really big rocket, and I too had been giving the subject a lot of thought. I had been with the heavy artillery. Artillery's highest achievement to date had been the huge Paris Gun, developed during the First World War. This could fire a 210-millimeter shell with about 23 pounds of high explosive about 80 miles. My idea of a first big rocket was something that would send a ton of explosive over 160 miles—that is, double the range of the Paris Gun. When I compared the enormous weight of the Paris Gun and the difficulties of rail transport and bringing into firing position with the insignificant weight of the equipment necessary for launching large rockets, when I considered the quantity of high explosive and the consequent increase of efficiency, it was clear to me that the military prospects of the rocket were extremely bright, provided that it could be given greater accuracy than the shells from the Paris Gun.

The conversation touched on one point after another. We were soon agreed on the need for a payload of 1 ton. A rough calculation showed that with elevation of 45 degrees on entering practically airless space, and a maximum velocity of 3350 miles per hour, the rocket might achieve a range of 172 miles.

We decided to go ahead with a first preliminary draft of the project. I stipulated a number of military requirements, among others, that the dispersion—that is, the distribution of 50 per cent of the impact points around the target point—should be 2 or 3 mils both longitudinally and laterally. This means that for every 1000 feet of range a deviation of only 2 or 3 feet either too far or too short was acceptable, and the same for lateral deviation. This was stricter than is customary for artillery, where a 50-per-cent dispersion of 4 to 5 per cent of the range is considered acceptable.

I limited the over-all size of the rocket, insisting that we must be able to transport it as a unit by road and that it must not exceed the maximum width laid down for road vehicles. If carried by rail the rocket must be able to pass through any railroad tunnel. These points determined the general dimensions. We all agreed from the start that a slenderer shape would involve less air resistance and give us greater range. However, practical consideration called for a sturdier body. It would be for the engineers to find the ideal shape.

We were counting on a rocket motor with a thrust of 25 to 30 tons. We might have designed Test Stand I for this figure, but as we did not relish the prospect of building new and bigger test stands every few years we decided to build the first one to take any motor up to 100 tons thrust.

The construction bureau under Riedel began designing our first large-scale rocket. A few weeks later the main features of the A-4 had been determined. We planned a take-off weight of about 12 tons. To achieve a thrust of about 25 tons for a burning time of 65 seconds, assuming an exhaust velocity of about 7000 feet per second, at least 8 tons of propellants were needed. This should result in a maximum velocity of about 1 mile per second. But at such high velocities it was imperative that we should be able to time Brennschluss to a fraction of a second. We should also have to find means of confining the lateral deviation of the missile to the prescribed dispersion. With a diameter of more than 5 feet the rocket would have to be over 45 feet long. The diameter measured over the tail fins must not exceed 11.48 feet.

I discussed the first design sketches with von Braun and Riedel. We were a bit uneasy, for we were up against a mass of new problems and quite aware that the step was really a little too ambitious. We suspected that it might take years to work out the best shape for this missile, which would have to exceed all the usual speeds of aircraft and projectiles. There would have to be research in subsonic and supersonic wind tunnels, and none existed then which came anywhere near such speeds. We should also have to change from pressure feeding to pump feeding; the weight of tanks strong enough to withstand the required pressure would be too great. Yet no pumps which would be light enough were then known. Nor were there any pumps which could deal with liquid oxygen at minus 185 degrees centigrade. And how were the pumps to be driven? By gas turbine? If so, ought it to be fed with exhaust gas from the combustion chamber or with gas provided in some other way? Nor was any instrument for measuring air speeds accurate enough to enable us to switch off at the right moment. Planning must needs be helplessly bogged at first in the morass of so many unsolved problems.

In July 1936 Dr. Hermann brought us the unfavorable results of a stability test in the Aachen wind tunnel on the first model of the A-3, and explained all the difficulties of finding the right fin shape for arrow-stabilized projectiles at supersonic speeds. We now decided to proceed very carefully step by step. Before continuing with the development of the A-4 we would await the results of the A-3 firings. We also wished, in developing the A-4, to follow the methods that had led to success with smaller rockets. We must make the motor first of all. We must find out, for a start, whether it was at all possible to build a chamber for thrust of such magnitude and to keep it working for some time. We must also seek to improve the performance of our motors in general.

Accordingly, we postponed the A-4 project as a whole. We decided, however, to forge ahead on the equipment needed for the large-scale plan. Development of the control mechanism and

individual components would go on concurrently, and these were
to be tested, for reasons of economy, in a smaller rocket. This—if
possible, the A-3—would have to incorporate all the experience
we hoped to obtain in the forthcoming test firings.

As we were anxious to get on with developing the big 25-ton
motor as soon as Test Stand I was finished at Peenemünde, we
put in an order immediately for exhaust nozzles—a necessary
precaution in view of long delivery dates and the difficulties of
production. When they were finally delivered eighteen months
later we had made such progress that the complete rocket motor
for A-4 was only half as long as the exhaust nozzle ordered in
the autumn of 1936.

This advance in motor development was mainly due to the
work of Dr. Walter Thiel, who had joined the Experimental Station West in the autumn of 1936—though von Braun and Riedel
also contributed many ideas. As successor to Dr. Wahmke in the
Research Branch of the Army Weapons Department, Dr. Thiel
had continued with basic research. Important decisions on the
best mixture ratio, the effect of incomplete combustion, the shape
to be given to the motor, and the choice of propellants were based
on his work.

Thiel, a pale-complexioned man of average height, with dark
eyes behind spectacles with black horn rims, fair hair brushed
straight back, and a strong chin, was an extremely hard-working,
conscientious, and systematic research worker. On occasional
visits to his office I had learned to rate both him and his methods
very highly. He gladly accepted our invitation to join us and
change over from basic research to applied research and development. He was put in complete charge of propulsion, with the aim
of creating a 25-ton motor.

To ensure complete combustion of the fuel before it reached the
nozzle we had hitherto made the combustion chamber quite
elongated, so that the time an individual fuel droplet remained in
the chamber would be as long as possible. The analysis of gases
in the jet seemed to indicate that we were right. Yet performance
did not improve. Until then we had been projecting fairly thick

fuel and oxygen jets against each other under pressure. The violent contact vaporized them and combustion then took place along the length of the chamber, with varying consistencies of mixture in different parts. Combustion was thus not homogeneous, and we could not prevent the chamber walls from burning through. We had this difficulty with every new chamber.

I suggested that we should try to achieve a very fine atomization of the separate propellants, by centrifugal injection nozzles, and that the vapor formed by both propellant components should be ignited after mixing. This would be bound to accelerate combustion, reduce length of the chamber, and improve performance, provided the mixture ratio was right.

Dr. Thiel set about developing this idea. He found a way by using special centrifugal nozzles. A few days later he demonstrated his injection system made up of these nozzles by connecting it to the faucet, and I thought he had found the solution. He submitted it to engineering colleges and institutes for research, and at the same time set about utilizing the system for the 1.5-ton motor. After a year's work he had reduced the length of this chamber from nearly 6 feet to about 1 foot. Exhaust speed was first increased to 6600 feet per second, then actually to 6900. The maximum exhaust speed possible in theory was 7500 feet per second. Specific fuel consumption dropped to 4.5 grams of propellant per second per kilogram of thrust. We had therefore made a considerable advance in motor development.

To be sure, we still had one serious headache. Improved combustion caused a rise in temperature, and the cooling surface had been decreased, so we were again faced with the old cooling difficulties. I suggested that the section leading from the cylindrical part of the chamber to the nozzle entrance should be made cone-shaped. The experiment was successful, and the chamber wall no longer burned through at this point. By removing the injection head from the combustion chamber, Dr. Thiel was able to produce a sort of mixing compartment and so keep the flame front at a distance from the brass injection nozzles. In this way any burning of the injection nozzles became impossible.

The 1.5-ton chamber design gave excellent results up to the maximum performance we could reasonably expect with a combustion pressure of 220 pounds per square inch. Above that working pressure we had no desire to go. We knew, of course, that performance would improve up to a pressure of 735 pounds per square inch, but that at still higher pressures improvement would be only slight. On the other hand, the weight of both the motor and the tanks would be substantially greater. The disadvantages canceled out the advantages. So we kept to a chamber pressure of 220 pounds per square inch.

Shortly after this Dr. Thiel developed a 4.5-ton motor. He placed three injection heads from the 1.5-ton chamber in various arrangements above the combustion chamber proper. The innovation was successful, for the high performance was maintained.

Yet the motors still burned through from time to time at points along the wall or at the throat of the nozzle. Dr. Thiel's engineer colleague, Pöhlmann, made a useful suggestion. How would it be if a sort of insulating layer were formed between the heat of the combustion flame and the wall? If we irrigated the inner wall of the chamber with alcohol, it would of course evaporate and burn, but the temperature of this layer could never equal that inside the chamber. Such was the origin of film cooling. A large number of small perforations at the endangered sections admitted alcohol to the motor and especially to the exhaust nozzle under slight pressure. The holes in the wall were filled, after drilling, with Wood's metal, which melted as soon as the flame formed, thus allowing the cooling alcohol to enter.

For the first time we had achieved full reliability.

When we later discussed the design and injection system of the 25-ton motor for the A-4, von Braun suggested placing eighteen uniform injection heads at the head of the chamber. Eighteen of the injection heads and mixing chambers developed by Dr. Thiel for the 1.5-ton chamber were arranged in two concentric circles. Thus we obtained the injection system for the big chamber, a matter that had given us so much trouble during our first planning. The first big chambers to be heat-tested in the spring of 1939 at Test Stand I at Peenemünde had this system.

At Kummersdorf, Dr. Thiel had been the first to venture on the use of welded sheet-steel chambers with walls 0.12 inches thick, instead of the aluminum hitherto used exclusively for the bigger chambers, and he had begun experiments with them in altitude chambers, and with a higher combustion-chamber pressure. He had some first-rate engineers in his section, among them Schluricke and Pöhlmann, who were a great help to him by taking the detail design work off his hands and making their own practical suggestions.

It was not easy to work with Dr. Thiel. He set his whole mind to the job but was tremendously ambitious and aware of his own worth. He took a superior attitude and demanded equal devotion to duty from his colleagues. I had to smooth over a good deal of friction.

In May 1937 we were able to move to Peenemünde most of the Kummersdorf staff, which had grown to over ninety. However, the test stands at Peenemünde were not yet working. Dr. Thiel therefore stayed on at Kummersdorf as branch chief on motors, with five assistants and a few mechanics. Not until the summer of 1940 did he come to Peenemünde to take charge of all the experimental work.

Meanwhile we had succeeded in getting hold of another very good brain for our project. Von Braun had stressed to me again and again the importance of having our own wind tunnel for supersonic speeds, as designed by Dr. Hermann. I agreed, but the cost frightened me; the estimate was 300,000 marks. I had had enough experience with building to know that there wasn't the least chance of the cost remaining at that figure, especially with von Braun about. The supersonic tunnel was more likely to cost a million marks.

At the end of September 1936, when Dr. Hermann finally brought records from the Aachen wind tunnel that proved the stability of the tail fins in the third model of the A-3, I determined to build our own tunnel, cost what it might. I went to see Becker and told him what we had in mind, stressing its vital importance. He asked what it would cost. When I named the sum he looked grave. Eventually he gave his agreement, but on one condition: at least one other division of the twelve within the Research and Development Section of the Army Weapons Department must show interest in the erection of a supersonic tunnel and agree to make use of it. That seemed easy enough to me. I was firmly convinced that a supersonic wind tunnel would cut the time devoted to pure trial-and-error development to an absolute minimum. The same must apply to artillery projectiles, and the Air Force for its part had nothing but praise for wind tunnels.

I went to see the heads of divisions and met only with refusals. Even the Ballistics and Munitions Division took no interest in getting the Army Weapons Department a wind tunnel of its own. They did not even change their tune when I promised that the tunnel would show us how to increase the range of every type of ordinary gun by at least 20 per cent by modifying the shape of shells.

Finally I had only one more division to see, that of anti-aircraft artillery. I knew the head of this division. It was he who at last gave me the endorsement I sought. Becker agreed, and the project of the Peenemünde supersonic tunnel, expected to be the most efficient in the world with respect to speed and size of working cross section, began to take shape in the woods of the island of Usedom. We managed to persuade Dr. Hermann to take charge of the tunnel, and he joined us on April 1, 1937.

Although the figures he had reported at the end of September 1936 enabled us to speed up construction and development of the A-3, another year passed before we could undertake actual test firing. Our time was wholly taken up with static tests of the motor, modification and testing of valves, tests on the assembled rocket with and without guidance equipment, tests on the parachute, development of the molybdenum jet vanes, construction of launching rack, and preparations on the Oie.

Now at last, in December 1937, we were ready. We launched

the A-3. The result of our years of labor was complete failure. What had gone wrong? Eye-witness accounts from the staff were wildly contradictory. Everyone claimed to have seen something different. We decided to venture on a second launching. From the lighthouse I watched the second rocket rise from the ground. The same thing happened again. Soon after the start it made almost a quarter-turn about its longitudinal axis, turned into the wind, and, after climbing a few hundred yards, ejected the parachute. Then the rocket motor stopped burning and the rocket fell into the sea near the steep east coast of the island.

In neither case could we determine the cause of failure from salvaged fragments. Could it have been the parachute? Was there something wrong with its release?

We agreed to leave the parachute out of the next two rockets. Then, suddenly, fog enveloped the island. One could not see two paces ahead. It lasted for days. We held discussions at the inn for hours on end. Everyone had his own theory. I finally decided that we must eliminate possible sources of failure one by one, starting with the parachute.

At last a freshening wind ended the fog. According to the weather forecast, rain, snow, gales, and a cold snap were to be expected within a few days. We had to hurry. But even the next two shots gave no better results. Immediately after rising the rocket took the line of least resistance, turned into the wind, and at a height of between 2500 and 3000 feet fell over and dropped into the sea.

We realized that the power of the control mechanism was not enough to withstand the aerodynamic forces. A northeast wind averaging 26 feet per second had been blowing, and the control gear had not been able to prevent the rocket from rotating from the very start.

We made calculations and tests. It turned out that even with a cross wind of 12 feet per second the control system was too weak to counterbalance the turning of the rocket about its longitudinal axis. The movement of the vanes was also too slow. The control gear developed at most 181 foot-pounds over a period of 2.8

seconds. Therefore, we ought, if possible, to increase power ten-fold and the speed of the vanes considerably.

As we ran into the Peene estuary in our motorboats late in the afternoon, when it was already getting dark and blowing hard, the icy northwesterly gale sent high black waves slapping down on the foredeck and over the superstructure. Rain and snow made visibility difficult. We were feeling subdued, almost despondent—but not hopeless. Despite all our failures we were still convinced that we would succeed.

The days and weeks that followed were devoted to discussions in the conference room of the Designing House at the Army Experimental Station. We had to determine what our next step was to be. In the end we decided to abandon the A-3 and proceed with a new rocket, the A-5, before continuing development of the A-4. The A-5 was to be given the well-tried rocket motor of the A-3; but the diameter of the rocket would be increased by 4 inches, though the over-all length would be the same. Above all, the control system would be improved. We did not expect the Kreisel-geräte G.m.b.H. to have modified control equipment ready in the near future. We therefore decided to install for a start the more powerful apparatus supplied by the firm of Siemens, which had come in on development a few months before. The rocket was also given a receiving set for Brennschluss and parachute-release signals. The tail surfaces were to be modified and shortened in accordance with the latest findings from wind-tunnel tests.

These new tail surfaces had no ring antenna, but wider fins, the inner edge of which curved outward below the exhaust nozzle. The new design was based on the following considerations: both the A-3 and the A-5 had the same motor and in its exhaust nozzle the combustion gases were to expand until pressure at the nozzle exit was 1 atmosphere, corresponding to air pressure at sea level. But we wished to reach greater altitudes. As air pressure would be considerably less in those regions, excess pressure in the exhaust would cause it to widen into a bell-like shape. The old tail surfaces of the A-3 might have caught fire as a result. Further, the air resistance of the new tail surfaces promised to be considerably less than that of the old ones with the ring. We might thus be able to exceed the speed of sound.

The stability of the A-5 with the new tail surfaces was now tested in the subsonic tunnel of the Zeppelin Aircraft Works at Friedrichshafen under the supervision of Dr. Schirmer, and then again in the supersonic tunnel at Aachen. After this, construction of the A-5 began and a few weeks later the first experimental units were built in the Peenemünde workshops.

My chief concern was to shorten the period between shots and to fire small experimental series. I therefore ordered A-5 production to be increased to ten units a month. We kept on hoping that these rockets might go through the sonic barrier. The great question was whether the increase in air resistance and changes in the center of gravity would cause oscillations powerful enough to shatter the rocket. At that time no measurements could be taken in any wind tunnel at the speed of sound itself, and no fin-stabilized body had maintained stability in flight at supersonic speeds without breaking up. We could only drop models of the A-5 from airplanes at a great height and see what happened.

We built several solid iron models about 8 inches in diameter and 5 feet in length. They weighed about 550 pounds and were equipped with various types of tail surfaces. We installed smoke composition and flares. In September 1938 we began to drop these missiles from a Heinkel He-111 at 20,000 feet. The trajectory was recorded by phototheodolites and cinetheodolites. At about 3000 feet the "bombs" attained a maximum speed of 800 miles per hour, thus exceeding the speed of sound.

We were gratified by this result. The oscillations we had seen in no case exceeded 5 degrees. We also worked on a braking parachute that would open at the peak of the trajectory if the rocket's speed was not over 250 miles per hour and would be capable of reducing this speed to about 45 miles per hour without tearing. The Graf Zeppelin Flight Research Institute at Stuttgart developed a ribbon parachute for us. We gave the A-5 two parachutes, one of the ribbon type for braking and one large one for support, which brought the rocket, after braking, safely to the ground at 15 feet per second. We had to make sure that the rocket did not break up on striking either ground or water, so that we could retrieve the unit undamaged and identify the cause in case of failure.

We repeated the experiments with dummy rockets dropped from aircraft, this time with built-in parachutes.

A newly hired technical draughtsman at Kummersdorf suggested using graphite vanes instead of the expensive molybdenum types. Dr. Thiel accepted the suggestion and made some successful tests. The price of a set of vanes thus fell from 150 to 1.5 marks, and graphite ones were adopted for the A-5.

Development was delayed many times because the control mechanisms were not ready. At Test Stand VI in Peenemünde, built as an exact replica of the big test stand at Kummersdorf, the individual components of the autopilot system were tested continuously while the rocket motor burned. Suggestions for improvements were sent to the manufacturers, alterations were carried out and tested, and the mechanism was modified repeatedly. In the summer of 1938 we decided to wait no longer for the final autopilot but to launch four uncontrolled A-5 rockets from the Greifswalder Oie in the autumn, to test the stability of the rocket itself during flight. No parachutes were used.

At these tests there was much less cross wind. There was some deflection, but the rockets reached almost the speed of sound and a height of 5 miles. They fell into the sea and were lost, but on the whole we were satisfied with the inherent stability of the A-5.

New ideas on allegedly better tail surfaces were continually cropping up. Our wind tunnel would probably not be in operation before the end of 1939. However, we thought it necessary to try out in the open air the trajectories worked out on the basis of previous wind-tunnel tests. Phenomena might occur in flight that we had not observed in the wind tunnel. Accordingly, a final large-scale launching of models with various types of stabilizing surfaces was scheduled at Peenemünde. We had a large number of small models manufactured by Hellmuth Walter in Kiel, with the proportions of the A-5 and the same center of gravity. We added the various forms of fins. These small rockets were given a hydrogen-peroxide motor. They were 8 inches in diameter and 5 feet long, had a deadweight of 60 pounds, and could take 45 pounds of hydrogen peroxide. Decomposition period was 15 seconds and thrust 260 pounds.

The propellant was run under pressure over a potassium-permanganate paste acting as a catalyst. An 85-per-cent solution of hydrogen peroxide was decomposed to generate superheated steam and oxygen. The reaction of this gas mixture, which emerged from the nozzle at the rate of nearly 3500 feet per second, gave the missile its motive power.

In March 1939 tests began at Peenemünde Bay and later on the Greifswalder Oie. They gave a graphic picture of the different flying capabilities of the models equipped with the various tail surfaces. As a rule these models were launched from a rack several yards long, but some, for better observation of their inherent stability, were simply sent up from a firing table without the rack. The results were practically the same.

The Walter motor, despite its low performance, enabled us by its simplicity and easy handling to test models in a long series of free flight at very low cost.

The tests proved that the best tail-surface design was that suggested by the wind-tunnel tests for the A-5. Compared with that of the A-3, this was considerably shorter and wider, but it turned out to be considerably thinner than was practice in aircraft construction. If we had simply adopted the ordinary aircraft type of tail surfaces, the airstream would have become turbulent at the high speeds we attained and the large angle of attack; consequently control and stability would have been impossible. We therefore had to go our own way in designing our aerodynamic surfaces.

All the experimental models had a tendency to turn into the wind and all showed some degree of rotation around the longitudinal axis. The same thing happened nearly every time. After a good distance of completely straight and stable flight they would begin to wobble, and always on the same steering fin. We decided the cause was that the turning of the model about its longitudinal axis finally came into resonance with the model's inherent oscillation about its transverse axis.

There were two possible ways of avoiding this: either to prevent the tendency to turn about the longitudinal axis by making suitable control adjustments; or, using small, simply constructed models, to have the rocket spin around its longitudinal axis so fast that no inherent oscillation would matter.

From the beginning of our experiments on control equipment for large rockets we had the first possibility in view. At all costs we had to keep the rocket from turning about its longitudinal axis during the powered section of the trajectory. With the A-4, the internal vanes were not sufficient for the purpose in the second third of the powered trajectory. We had to add external air vanes to obtain a sufficient amount of control torque.

At the end of October 1939 a new series of tests began on the Oie. There had been great changes on the island in the meantime. Sleeping quarters had been built. Facing north, in the direction of the firing site, stood the long and massive Measurement House, dazzlingly white in the sunshine, with its workshop, oscillograph room, offices, and flat roof reached by an outside stairway. There were concrete roads, concrete observation bunkers, and a concrete apron of considerably enlarged size. The scaffolding covered with awnings had been replaced by a sheet-metal-covered working tower, which could be wholly closed in and tilted flat for the take-off. To bring the rocket, painted bright yellow and red, into firing position, it was pushed through the detachable roof of the lowered tower and both were then raised by means of a cable winch. The rocket was then let down by a pulley block onto the firing table, which stood exactly beneath the center of the tower.

The phototheodolite pivots had been supplemented by cine-theodolite towers. A network of cables for light, telephone communication, measurement, and power covered all important points of the island. The storage tent had been replaced by a big corrugated iron shed. Submarine cables connected the island with measurement points on Rügen and with points at the northern and southern ends of the island of Usedom.

Three rockets were to be launched, two vertically, the third planned to tilt. They were equipped with Siemens control gear. On a bright, sunny day in late autumn, beside an unruffled blue sea, the first rocket shot up from the firing table. It rose vertically in the azure sky. It did not turn about its longitudinal axis and did not turn into the wind. The missile rose steadily higher and higher, faster and faster on its course.

The backs of our necks ached as we stared aloft, following the trajectory. The rocket rose to 2, to 2½, to 3 miles, and farther still. At a height of nearly 5 miles, after 45 seconds of burning, the tanks ran dry and brought propulsion to an end. The speed of the rocket caused it to rise still higher.

At last it reached the peak of its course and slowly turned over. At that moment von Braun pressed the button transmitting the radio signal for parachute release, and a tiny white point appeared close to the flashing, sunlit body of the rocket. This was the braking parachute. Precisely 2 seconds later von Braun pressed another button, which released the big supporting parachute.

The rocket, which after all the alterations incorporated now weighed nearly 2000 pounds, glided slowly down, hanging quietly from the shrouds. The light easterly wind drove it toward the harbor, and after a few minutes it dropped in the water outside the mole with a splash that glittered in the sunshine. The missile rose to the surface, stern upward. The empty tanks would keep it afloat for about 2 hours.

Our launch immediately left the harbor and in little more than half an hour the rocket, its bright paint easily seen among the dark waves, was hauled aboard.

The second launching on the following day gave almost exactly similar results. The rocket was taken from the water only a few hundred yards from the same spot.

We still dared not congratulate ourselves. Only the next test could tell us for certain whether the main problem, namely that of guiding the rocket in a prescribed direction, could be accomplished.

The axis of the gyroscope, which had hitherto kept the rocket vertical, was to be slowly inclined in the target direction by a pre-set clockwork mechanism. The control equipment was designed to compensate any tendency to deviate from the direction steadily maintained in space by the gyroscope axis.

This procedure, which produces the tilt needed for firing over great distances, may be visualized about as follows. The axis of one gyroscope is tilted by electrical or mechanical means in the direction of the target. The control mechanism of the rocket then seeks by means of the vanes to keep the rocket's longitudinal axis parallel to the axis of the gyroscope. Therefore the rocket does not continue on its vertical path but moves in the direction "prescribed" for any moment by the slowly moving axis of the gyroscope. The result is movement along a curve.

On the third launching the rocket was to start vertically and the tilt would begin very gradually after a few seconds of vertical climbing. We had often tested the procedure during static firings of the rocket at the test stands, but we were now looking forward to the real thing with great excitement. The experiment was wholly successful. After 4 seconds of vertical climb the rocket began slowly to tilt its nose toward the east. It crossed the Oie at increasing speed and flew in a lofty arc over the sea. At the peak of the trajectory, about 4 miles away from the starting point and at a height of 2½ miles, the parachute was released. Once more the missile dropped slowly from the sky into the surging waters of the Baltic. This rocket, too, was recovered.

We had at last achieved a great success. True, we had not yet reached the speed of sound, but our calculations had been proved correct. We had shown that the liquid-propellant rocket was equal to the tasks set for it. Seven years after starting work we had created the A-5, a unit which, since it could be recovered, enabled us to test the many interior mechanisms required for the large-scale rocket in actual flight. We could now develop these mechanisms for incorporation in the A-4.

At later launchings with the A-5 we achieved a range of 11 miles and a height of 7½ miles.

I could now breathe again. On September 5, when I had gone with General Becker to make my report to Colonel General von Brauchitsch, Commander-in-Chief of the Army, at his headquarters in camp at Zossen and to request his endorsement of the A-4 project as one of national importance, I hadn't felt too comfortable. What would happen if all our hopes should prove illusory?

Now, however, I could see our goal clearly, and the way that led to it. I now knew that we should succeed in creating a weapon with far greater range than any artillery. What we had successfully done with the A-5 must be equally valid, in improved form, for the A-4.

CHAPTER 6

HITLER AND THE ROCKET

In March 1939 Hitler saw for the first time the work we had been doing on liquid-propellant rockets. On a cold, wet day, with an overcast sky and water still dripping from the rain-drenched pines, he arrived, accompanied by von Brauchitsch and Becker, at the experimental station of Kummersdorf West. When I reported to him at the entrance to the station in front of the great wooden shed, I immediately had the impression that his thoughts were elsewhere. As he shook hands with me his eyes seemed to look through me to something beyond. His remarkably tanned face, with the unsightly snub nose, little black mustache, and extremely thin lips, showed no sort of interest in what we were to show him.

While I spoke he kept his eyes fixed steadfastly on me. I still don't know whether he understood what I was talking about. Certainly he was the only visitor who had ever listened to me without asking questions.

We went over to the old test stand to witness a test run of a rocket motor developing a thrust of 650 pounds. The horizontally suspended combustion chamber was ignited. When the harsh roar of the pale blue jet of gas, concentrated in a narrow stream with the supersonic shock waves clearly delineated in colors of varying brightness, caused a painful vibration in our eardrums in spite of thick wads of cottonwool, his expression did not change. Nor did the next demonstration, with a vertically suspended motor developing a thrust of 2200 pounds, draw a single word from him. Hitler watched this test run, standing behind a protective wall, from a distance of only 30 feet.

64

On the way to one of the assembly towers at the third test stand I told him about our work at Peenemünde and of the results we had achieved. The Führer of the German people walked on beside me, staring ahead and holding his tongue.

In the assembly tower we had assembled a cutaway model of the A-3 horizontally on low wooden trestles. One could see, through slits and holes in the thin outer sheet-metal skin, the standpipes, valves, tanks, and the rocket motor, and observe the flow of propellants and the control processes. To make it easier to understand, related components were painted the same color. While Hitler was looking into the rocket von Braun gave technical explanations, describing how the entire system worked. Hitler examined the machine very closely from all sides and finally turned away, shaking his head.

I mentioned that Aggregates 3 and 5 (A-3 and A-5) were for research purposes only and were not intended for use in war or to carry any payload.

At a third demonstration run at the big test stand we showed a vertically suspended A-5 rocket without skin and fins but with control mechanism in operation. We then went into the adjoining shed, where I gave Hitler more information about Aggregate 4 in the presence only of his intimates. He listened with apparent interest but again in silence.

During lunch in the mess I sat diagonally opposite Hitler. As he ate his mixed vegetables and drank his habitual glass of Fachingen mineral water, he chatted with Becker about what they had seen. I couldn't tell much from what was said, but he seemed a little more interested than during the demonstration or immediately after. He asked casually how long it might take to develop the A-4, and about its range. When I named the long peacetime standard periods he answered with a brief nod. Finally he wanted to know whether we could use steel sheeting instead of aluminum. When I did not reject the possibility but emphasized that it would cause delay, he looked past me with an absent smile and uttered the one word of appreciation that was to be vouchsafed to us.

"Es war doch gewaltig!" ("Well, it was grand!")

He then referred to Max Valier, saying he had got to know him fairly well in Munich and had heard from him what the rocket's prospects were thought to be. He called Valier a dreamer. Contradiction would have been out of place, as Hitler couldn't bear it, and I should also have embarrassed von Brauchitsch and Becker. So I had no choice but to explain that we were, of course, only at the very beginning of rocket development and that its present stage corresponded with the first steps in aviation. Valier, Oberth, Goddard, and others, I said, were to space travel what Lilienthal had been to the airplane and Zeppelin to the airship. Both these, I continued, had reached their present state only after a long period of development.

Hitler did not consider that the airship had been a great invention. I asked him whether he had been on board one.

"No," he answered after a moment's thought. "Nor shall I ever get into an airship. The whole thing," he went on, "always seems to me like an inventor who claims to have discovered a cheap new kind of floor covering which looks marvelous, shines forever, and never wears out. But he adds that there is one disadvantage. It must not be walked on with nailed shoes and nothing hard must ever be dropped on it because, unfortunately, it's made of high explosive." Then he repeated, "No, I shall never get into an airship."

On taking leave of me beside his car he shook hands and briefly thanked me. I did not know whether to be pleased or not. The whole visit seemed to me strange, if not downright unbelievable. In all the years I had been working on rocket development this was the first time that anyone had witnessed the massive output of gas at enormous speed, in luminous colors, from a rocket exhaust, and heard the thunderous rumble of power thus released, without being enraptured, thrilled, and carried away by the spectacle.

At least we could be glad that everything we had shown had been in good working order. We had to be content with that reflection. Colonel General von Brauchitsch and the few others who had seen the demonstration had given honest and unqualified expression to their admiration and approval of what we had accomplished in so few years. We did not think, however, that we had succeeded in arousing Hitler's interest.

I simply could not understand why this man, who always showed the greatest interest in all new weapons, who found no gun or tank too difficult, who when new guns were demonstrated could hardly be induced to leave and wanted all technical details explained, had shown no sign of enthusiasm on his visit to us. Why that brain, equipped, so far as all questions of armament were concerned, with a positively staggering memory for figures, could not take in the true significance of our rockets remained a mystery to me.

I was sure that he appreciated the novelty as such, but that he did not grasp its bearing on the future. He could not fit the rocket into his plans, and what was worse for us at that time, did not believe the time was ripe for it. He certainly had no feeling for technological progress, upon which the basic conditions for our work depended. The engineering spectacle had no doubt fascinated him to some extent, if one might draw that inference from his comment that it had been "grand." It was this, perhaps, that made him let us go on with the work; but he did not then appear to foresee any possibility of our plans being realized, or even a practical application for a giant rocket.

How different from the impulsive, easily excited, optimistic Goering, who always saw everything in the rosiest colors, and in doing so invariably overshot the mark! When a few weeks later he witnessed a similar demonstration in Kummersdorf he slapped his thigh, laughing and beaming, and made fantastic prophecies. He immediately foresaw all sorts of future possibilities for air travel and shipbuilding, rail and road traffic, which could never in any circumstances be realized.

I found it very difficult to convince him that fuel consumption would make such schemes fantastically uneconomic. When I explained to him that economic operation could be achieved only at a speed several times that of sound and in practically airless space, he failed to understand me. His mind, in other respects so highly imaginative, was unable to pass beyond the earth's atmosphere.

CHAPTER 7

A MAN CALLED DEGENKOLB

The dismissal of the Commander-in-Chief of the Army, Field Marshal von Brauchitsch lost us one of our most useful backers. His wise foresight and clear appreciation of the tactical possibilities of our weapon had moved him in September 1939 to give us highest military priority. When Hitler had struck us from the priority list in the spring of 1940, von Brauchitsch had repeatedly urged the military importance of our work. But it was all in vain. In the months that followed, when our best men were being called up and we faced complete suspension, the Field Marshal, at my suggestion and without Hitler's knowledge, had allowed us to draw from the fighting troops four thousand technically qualified men, engineers and laborers, for work at Peenemünde. We thus created the Northern Experimental Command, an operational unit detailed for temporary service on the home front. The soldiers were given only work suited to their previous training, and being classified as front-line troops they were, even when outside Peenemünde, beyond the reach of the civilian authorities. Von Brauchitsch's high sense of responsibility and imagination in taking this step played a decisive part in the continuance of our work.

From March 27, 1942, onward, and especially after the brilliantly successful experiment on October 3, 1942, which aroused no echoes, we sent one memorandum after another, eight copies of each, to the highest authorities, both civilian and military.

If the A-4 were to be in operation by December 1943 there was not a moment to be lost in planning production, forming and training new units, and building launching sites. For these purposes it was necessary for us to be included in the top priorities list of urgent state projects.

I learned through the grapevine that exists in all armies that in high places, including the highest, the general opinion of our plans was unfavorable. Even my immediately superior officers began to doubt whether our ideas could be carried through on a large scale. The very head of the Army Weapons Department, General Becker, only two days before he committed suicide because of a quarrel with Hitler, observed resignedly, "I only hope that I have not been mistaken in my estimate of you and your work." In view of my own unshakable faith and confidence these words were hard to bear, particularly when I thought of the dozens of reports, memorandums, and petitions in which we had vainly begged for our requirements to be met. So long as we did not head the list of priorities there was no prospect of getting the necessary allocation of raw materials and technical staff. We needed production planners, designers, and engineers, and we needed them at once.

Our requirements far exceeded the supplies our Army superiors could allocate on the home front. They extended into the field of administration of the Ministry of Munitions and needed the consent of Adolf Hitler.

The supreme authority treated us to delaying tactics. Since the beginning of the war, despite insistent representations, we had always been allotted just enough to keep us barely alive. I pressed for a decision. Either the state must make up its mind at last to put the A-4 project into operation in earnest, in which case we should have to be trusted and helped, or else work on the long-range rocket ought to be given up and the Peenemünde equipment used for something that was considered more urgent.

So extensive a program as that of the A-4, I continued to insist, could be successfully put through only on the basis of a reasonably consistent policy. The constant changes in priority grades had caused us endless difficulties. It was impossible to carry out our complex program according to plan. Essential building projects were not begun or had to be left unfinished; factory space and equipment were put into operation very late or not at all. Much time was wasted in searching for makeshift solutions when the straightforward way would have done the trick quicker and far more reasonably. Important requests remained unanswered. This situation, which prevented us from living and did not allow us to die, had now lasted for years and must come to an end if our long-range rocket was to be employed at all in the current war.

Ever since the huge bomber losses during the attack on England in 1940, my colleagues and I had been firmly convinced that defeat in the air on the western front could be prevented, if at all, only by the employment of guided missiles of very great range and effect. In the long run the Luftwaffe would not be able to afford the continued loss of valuable flying crews.

The threadbare argument that our A-4 was too costly in comparison with the heavy bomber became more and more difficult to uphold in the light of experience over England. If, as accurate statistics showed, a bomber was shot down after an average of five or six flights over England, if it could carry only a total of six to eight tons of bombs during its active existence, and if the total loss of a bomber, including the cost of training the crew, were estimated at about thirty times the price of an A-4 (38,000 marks), then it was obvious that the A-4 came off best. It should have been only a question of time before this was recognized even at top level.

From hour to hour I awaited the supreme authority's blessing.

At last the august decision was given, and it almost knocked me out. Development was to proceed, and meanwhile production should be planned on paper, but nothing was said about raising our priority rating or ordering the Ministry of Munitions to give us all possible assistance. The strangest feature of this high-level decision was, however, an order to recall and destroy all memorandums, and even blueprints, except for three copies of the latter.

Valuable time was lost. I returned to Peenemünde from one of my begging expeditions almost in desperation. I explained the situation to Colonel Zanssen, Dr. von Braun, and the executives of the Army Experimental Station. I asked yet again that no effort should be spared to produce fresh and convincing proofs at the firing table. If we could show real results, I might still be able to find some way of altering this fatal, feeble decision.

Besides this we must at all costs find ways and means of shortening the time lag, inevitable with any new weapon, between completion of prototype and actual production.

I could see the time coming when the immeasurably stronger defences of the British Island would make flying over it impossible. Then, of course, production of our long-range weapon could not get going fast enough and no output would not be high enough. We should therefore have to start production planning at once, even before test shots began, and get on with it as fast as we could. For this purpose it was necessary to explore production possibilities—to get in touch without delay with the industry concerned, arouse its interest, and induce it to embark at once on imaginative collaboration with a view to possible mass production later.

I knew well enough the good and bad points of my colleagues and the Peenemünde organization. It was a research station, whose young and devotedly loyal research men were totally lacking in experience of how to transfer to mass production a thing like the A-4, unique in its complexity and with all its novel auxiliary ground equipment. The transition from prototype to mass production requires management by an experienced industrial production engineer, who will get out blueprints, plan and organize the start of production, make any further industrial preparations required, and place subcontracts in consultation with the cognizant branches of the Army Weapons Department.

Dr. von Braun proposed setting up a Production Planning Directorate. I managed to get for this task a qualified engineer, Stahlknecht, a special commissioner of the Ministry of Munitions, who had just completed his latest assignment and was now free. He had had a great deal of experience in the organization of conveyor-belt aircraft production. The large hall of our test building was earmarked as the assembly room for mass production. I also finally managed to interest Dr. Eckener of the Zeppelin Works, and he agreed to put his Friedrichshafen establishment at our disposal as a second assembly center.

I breathed again. But it was only a few weeks before I realized that without higher priorities we could accomplish nothing. We could not get on without the active support of the Ministry of Munitions. Our far-reaching plans had no sooner taken the first steps toward accomplishment than they were held up. The attempt to supplement the "paper" plans by practical preparations for production in the factories failed because of our inability to obtain allocations and the intolerably distant delivery dates, which were all we could get at our low priorities. We were especially hampered by our inability to obtain technical personnel.

Application after application went to high levels.

At the beginning of December 1942 I determined to make a vigorous personal appeal to Speer, Minister of Munitions, relying on the successful trial of October 3, which had justified our work. I expected that Speer, a special favorite of Hitler's, would be able to persuade the Führer to come to a decision.

In agreement with my colleagues I proposed to demand, for the whole project, approval of the scheme of March 27, 1942, the allocation of higher priorities, permission to start building a long-promised launching site on the Channel coast, estimated to take a year to complete, and the creation of a special production committee under Stahlknecht within the jurisdiction of the Ministry of Munitions, which would give us ministerial assistance in dealing with the German armaments industry.

During my Christmas leave I learned from Major Thom, head of the technical section of my divisional staff, that he had suddenly been ordered by Speer to go to the Channel coast with Dr. Steinhoff to reconnoiter a site near Watten. The launching site was to be built by the Todt organization. My interview had been fixed for the beginning of January at the Ministry of Munitions in Berlin, and I traveled there filled with hope and equipped with plenty of arguments.

On Janaury 8, 1943, in company with von Braun, I again ad-

dressed Speer on the subject of rocket development and preparations for tactical employment. We had built at Peenemünde, to a
scale of 1/100, a wooden model of the launching site, also models
of the vehicles of one detachment required for motorized employment of the long-range rocket, so that we could demonstrate
easily what work was required on ground installations and describe operational procedure. I was still waiting for Hitler's decision on my December proposal.

"The Führer cannot give your project higher priority yet,"
Speer informed me. "He is still not convinced that your plan will
succeed."

I was flabbergasted. Once more all the trouble had been in vain.
In my anger, I was tempted to thump the table with my fist. Why
in heaven's name was I not allowed to speak? Were we to lose
still more time? I could not and would not believe it.

Speer went on, "As head of the Todt organization I will take
it on myself to start at once with the building of the launching
site on the Channel coast. I hope," he continued, "that the Führer
will agree later on after all. The Todt organization knows all
about it. Please deal direct with Todt headquarters in Berlin."

I made a final appeal. "May I inquire, Minister, whether the
Führer has read any part of our memorandum of March last year?
Does he agree to the scale of the project as planned?"

Speer answered that Hitler had read the memorandum but
was still not convinced. So far as the jurisdiction of the Home
Forces was concerned, I should surely have no difficulty. "In the
military field, at any rate, your plans should be met. As for industry, you will have to try to manage with the aid of someone I
will introduce you to—Degenkolb, chairman of the Locomotives
Special Committee."

A lot I cared for Degenkolb and his locomotives! I was determined not to give in. "Minister, all I can do here and now is to
emphasize yet again that the whole project will be doomed to
ruin unless we are supplied at once with all the raw materials we
need, the industrial capacity, the building equipment, and, above
all, the technical personnel. Years of bitter experience have

taught us that nothing but higher priorities will get these for us."

My reproaches made no impression on Speer. All he did was come back to this man Degenkolb.

"You had better discuss all that with Degenkolb. He is to set up an A-4 production committee. He has shown such drive and ruthlessness that he can manage the seemingly impossible without any high priorities, purely on the power of his name and personality."

I retorted that no one would be better pleased than I if he succeeded, but, with all due respect, I knew the difficulties from my own experience. Speer shrugged his shoulders.

"You can trust Degenkolb. He has a reputation to lose."

"So have I, Minister. I also have a reputation to lose. But I can't feel any confidence—"

At these words the Minister left the room.

In came a man of middle height and middle age. He had a well-nourished appearance. In his round, sallow face, the obliquely set, keen blue eyes darted restlessly hither and thither. Prominent swellings above his eyebrows and the clearly marked veins in his temples were evidence of a hasty temper. This was Degenkolb, one of the closest associates of our greatest adversary in the Ministry of Munitions, Saur, the all-powerful Hauptamtsleiter (chief of the regional Party Office).

Degenkolb's completely bald and spherical head, his soft, loose cheeks, bull neck, and fleshy lips revealed a tendency toward good living and sensual pleasures, while the restlessness of his powerful hands and the vigor of his movements were evidence of vitality and mental alertness. He was never still. His reputation as the creator of the war locomotive stood high. But whether Degenkolb, who for all his drive and technical competence was really a primitive man of action, would be the right partner for me and my more intellectual colleagues remained to be seen. For the nonce he and I would be together under the same yoke.

All the time I was briefing him about our plans, the organization I had set up, and the A-4 program, I was wondering where I had heard the name Degenkolb before. Degenkolb, Degenkolb . . .

I linked the name with something unpleasant but couldn't think what it was. I explained Stahlknecht's task as special representative of the Ministry of Munitions in the sphere of production and added that responsibilities ought to be clearly defined. Some presentiment caused me to warn him that friction would have to be avoided at all costs. In conclusion I appealed for his vigorous help and stated our wishes, already so well known. "If you can and will help us, we shall soon achieve concrete success without any big changes in organization."

I noticed that Degenkolb had an absent air and did not even listen to some of my remarks. Nevertheless, he was outwardly most friendly. He said he did not believe difficulties would arise in any connection, either with Stahlknecht or my organization. Degenkolb, I thought, Degenkolb . . . Degenkolb . . . He would go to work, he said, in quite a different way. He intended to establish, on the analogy of the locomotive committee, an A-4 committee, with subcommittees for development, raw materials, management, subassemblies, ground organization, building projects, direction of labor, etc. Some of my senior subordinates would be appointed heads of these subcommittees.

I suggested that it might be a good idea for Degenkolb first of all to have a look at the A-4, meet the chiefs of my technical departments, and find out what their wishes were. I emphasized that we had at our disposal a streamlined, experienced, and capable organization already dealing with many of his suggested spheres of action. I kept my gaze fixed upon his fleshy face while I told him that if we were to work together we must stick strictly to the rules. I had, I reminded him, asked for help in getting materials, not for personal help. To set up a new ministerial body with the same tasks as our own, or working in parallel, would lead to complete failure, especially if the same people were employed in both. No man could serve two masters; that could only mean friction. Progress would be possible only if we understood each other and allowed no bad feeling or dispute to arise between us. After this I felt I ought to say something amiable.

"I put my trust in your drive as a chairman of committee in the

Ministry of Munitions, in your reputation, and in your great industrial experience." This last, I added, was exactly what we still urgently needed.

Degenkolb shook hands and promised to work in the closest possible collaboration with me. Then he started telling me about his great successes as chairman of the locomotive production committee.

While he was talking I found myself admiring his energy, his achievements, and his ideas. The man understood the art of persuasion. If only the indications of conceit and the repulsive complacency had not been so clearly evident! His drive seemed to me too forced, too portentous, too nearly allied to menace. Many of his phrases indicated a cynically unsympathetic attitude to any organization or scheme which he had not started himself. His claims to exclusive competence were brutally stressed. I listened attentively and was on my guard. Degenkolb seemed to belong to that brand of industrialist who automatically assumes that anyone in uniform must be reactionary, narrow-minded, and in need of enlightenment. I could already see some stiff fights ahead, certainly with my stubborn young colleagues. Then, suddenly, I knew!

I recalled with a shock that Degenkolb's name had been linked in the spring of 1940 with the suicide of General Becker, head of the Army Weapons Department, a man I had revered. Was it not Degenkolb who, after the sudden appointment of Todt as Minister of Munitions and shortly before Becker's death, had given emphatic and eloquent expression, in a speech made to representatives of the Army and of industry, to his bitter hatred of the Army Weapons Department and its officers and had made no secret of his contempt for all industrial work initiated or directed by the Army? Was it not he who had laid great stress on the alleged incompetence of the military organization as it existed then?

The new catchwords, "self-governing industry" and "direction of industry by industry," had been translated into action at that time, and had caused wholesale reorganization of the armaments industry, which until then had been directed by the Army Weapons Department. The Ministry of Munitions had been formed as an independent organization, on a par with the Weapons Departments of the three Services and the Armament Office of the Forces High Command.

This Ministry was staffed at the outset only by men from the Technical Office of the Nazi Party, with a few representatives of industry. Friction increased from day to day between the Ministry and the Army Weapons Department. I now suddenly remembered what astonishing diplomatic talents the chief of the Army Weapons Department had been compelled to develop during the reorganization to hold his ground against a Ministry endowed to the fullest extent with special powers, and to retain in the end, outwardly at least, his overriding and directing position in relation to the armaments industry. I had been unable to understand at the time why the new Ministry, linked only with the Army Weapons Department, had been created at all. To strengthen the Army Weapons Department itself by recruiting men from industry and the scientific world would certainly have achieved the desired result with less expense, delay, and muddle. The totalitarian claims of the Party's Technical Office and the profound feeling in industry against Army influence—I cannot absolve industry from blame—prevented this simple solution.

So the man who sat opposite me now was the very person whose powerful support of Todt and Saur had enabled them, despite intense opposition from the Army Weapons Department and their technically qualified officers, to bring about so fundamental a reorganization of the German armaments industry.

Degenkolb talked on and on. I believed I could dimly see a course of action. I was well aware of the solidarity of the departments in my charge, of their firm loyalty to me, and of my own expert knowledge and experience. Our combined weight would enable me, I was sure, to hold the balance against Degenkolb, given mutual sincerity and understanding.

We arranged to go to Peenemünde together the following day. Just as I was going to my car Saur appeared and accosted me.

"I suppose you think you've struck it lucky today, now that you've got your special committee at last. But don't be too sure. Trees have never grown as high as heaven yet. You haven't yet convinced or won me over, any more than you have the Führer!"

These were the people I was to work with to turn the A-4 into a weapon.

CHAPTER 8

"SOLDIERS, INC."

Degenkolb inspected Peenemünde. He saw an A-4 about to take off and in flight. The effect was the same upon him as upon any other human being. The first impression was overpowering. The talks that followed positively bubbled over with optimism and readiness to collaborate. He inspected the experimental missile assembly hall and visited our many workshops, giving brief advice here and there for the improvement of working processes and bold suggestions for simplifying construction. We listened to him in silence, as to an experienced works manager. Von Braun and Thiel told him that what he had seen was a first prototype model, brought to the working stage after toil and care, and as such much too complicated to be put into regular production. The simplified rocket earmarked for manufacture, Degenkolb was most respectfully told, would have passed its tests in a few months. The rocket being wholly automatic, every structural alteration had to be tested before being incorporated. We added that the slightest variation allowed to pass untested would be sure to lead to an explosion and failure of the rocket in flight. Alterations could only be introduced one at a time, for the simple reason that every failure so completely destroyed the missile that investigation of the trouble became almost impossible.

Stahlknecht showed Degenkolb his production schedule, under which he would deliver initially three hundred A-4's a month, beginning in January 1944. Within the following six months output could be raised to six hundred a month. Stahlknecht flattered Degenkolb very cleverly, mentioning the improvements we might expect from his personal assistance.

After staying a few hours Degenkolb went back to Berlin to set up his special A-4 committee. He relied for its composition on his well-tried locomotive builders. Despite my worries, he included certain of my own technical staff. A few days later he sent us his program. It would begin by October 1943, with three hundred A-4's a month, rising to nine hundred a month by December—a breathtaking acceleration that caused us to shake our heads. The worst of it was that the A-4 was to go into production exactly as Herr Degenkolb had seen it. Even if we instantly obtained all the assistance we had hitherto demanded in vain, the program was a mere illusion.

At the beginning of February 1943 I was summoned to the Ministry of Munitions in Berlin to meet Professor Hettlage, the departmental chief in charge of financial and organizational problems of the German armaments industry. At first I couldn't see the point of this urgently worded summons. When, on February 3, I found myself sitting, with a somewhat puzzled air, opposite Professor Hettlage, he called in Mackels, the representative of the Ministry of Munitions for Stettin, and a director named Kunze, acting for Degenkolb. Hettlage, still a young man, had Center Party antecedents and was a former City Treasurer of Berlin. At that time he was easily the most powerful man in the Ministry. He observed me for a time with his unusually large, clear, glittering blue eyes. Then, smiling politely, he embarked on a subject which, to say the least, was the last I expected the Ministry of Munitions to raise.

"Colonel," Hettlage began, "I have invited you here to discuss the best way of transforming the Army establishment at Peenemünde into a private stock company."

I was thunderstruck. I saw at once that the battle for Peenemünde had entered on a new and decisive stage as a result of Degenkolb's activities. So long as development of the A-4 was a gamble people only smiled at our efforts and called us unworldly idealists. Since no one had been bold enough to make an end of us we had been graciously tolerated. Now, however, it seemed to the gentlemen on top that after all there was "something in that

A-4." One never knew; the thing had possibilities. And they now felt that the time was ripe to put Peenemünde in their pocket. It really would not do for a creation like the A-4, which had every prospect of starting a new technical era, to be exploited by an establishment in the hands of the Army. The enterprise now required a different trademark. Fame and profit were on the way. I now knew where I was; the interest of the Party's Technical Office and of industry had been aroused and they were taking the offensive. I was determined to defend our Peenemünde. It ought not to be so difficult to discover the men behind the scenes and their motives and intentions. My question was brief.

"May I ask from whom the suggestion came?"

"The plan," Hettlage answered, "owes its origin to a proposal of Herr Degenkolb's." Just as I had thought.

"May I inquire how it is proposed to make the change?"

"We would transform Peenemünde into a stock company with limited liability. The entire capital of the company would remain for the present in the hands of the state, while the firm would be managed by a large concern acting as trustee—for instance, General Electric, Siemens, Lorenz, or Rheinmetall—with a view to transferring the plant, after amortization of the capital invested, to the possession of the firm."

A truly monstrous scheme!

"Are you aware," I inquired innocently, "that the value of Peenemünde, including everything spent on the place so far, is several hundred million marks? The interest payments and amortization quotas could hardly be a temptation to industry."

"We already have acceptable tenders," Hettlage explained. "We would make a cut in capital and declare assets of between one and two millions, letting the rest go."

What a charming idea! You take an investment running into several hundred million marks and turn it, by a "cut in capital," into a bargain of between one and two millions. Good business!

"Is it your opinion, then," I replied, "that this purely experimental plant, which has done nothing but cost money so far and has no facilities for mass production, will ever show any sort of profit or even pay for itself?"

"If it were asosciated with a big concern which could manufacture elsewhere as well, I consider it perfectly possible. Development costs would then be allowed for in the figures for quantity production and charged up."

It was incredible that I was dealing with officials and not ordinary swindlers. Public funds are of no account if you are set on doing the state, that is, the people, out of control of a business!

"With an annual budget of a hundred and fifty million marks," I suggested, "the price per unit would go up a good deal. The Peenemünde concern will always have to be supported by state subsidies."

"You will be good enough to leave me to deal with that," replied Hettlage curtly.

"May I ask why the conversion is proposed just at this moment?" I demanded.

"The reason is," Hettlage retorted, "that the establishment does not meet the requirements of a modern, well-organized factory run on economic lines. The management of the place is a failure." After the suggestions he had just made, this professor actually dared to utter the word "economic"! Who was he to judge whether the management had been a failure?

"I wish to state again, Professor, that we are dealing with a purely experimental establishment where perhaps out of a hundred projects only one leads to success and all the rest prove useless. That costs money."

"That's not what I mean," Hettlage retorted impatiently. "The expert personnel released for Peenemünde are not being fully employed or given tasks appropriate to their training and qualifications. We can't afford that sort of thing in wartime when technicians are so short."

I needed no such answer from Hettlage to enable me to see through his game. Instead of frankly stating that the intention was to take Peenemünde away from the Army, Professor Hettlage preferred to make an impertinent charge. The whole squalid scheme was now deplorably obvious. I wondered whether Degenkolb, since even he had failed to find us the technicians we needed, was trying to clear himself at our expense. I still do not know how I managed to answer Hettlage without losing my temper.

"That is a serious charge to make against the management. It may of course happen that some specialist engineer is temporarily transferred to a short-handed department if his appointed job seems unlikely to produce results of value to the general scheme. It may also happen that a specialist engaged for a certain job turns up before his department is ready for him, because it is short of materials. Naturally he has to pitch in somewhere else. This happens in any business. May I ask who makes these complaints?"

"Herr Mackels can tell you."

This was the cue for Mackels to intervene.

"Members of the Peenemünde employment group" he bleated, "have been complaining for months to me, as the Defense Sector representative, that staff members are not being used to full capacity and are not being given work for which they are qualified."

I turned to look straight at the Stettin representative of the Ministry of Munitions.

"You tell me, Herr Mackels, that these complaints have been reaching you for months. Why have I not been told of them until today?" I raised my voice and went on angrily, "Herr Mackels, your behavior is nothing short of extraordinary. The moment you had the first letter, your duty as armaments supply delegate was to approach the managing director at Peenemünde, give him the full name of the writer, and demand redress. I am certain there would have been no more complaints. I resent your action, sir."

Hettlage cut in, "Colonel, there is no question of your resenting anything. Herr Mackels is a representative of the Ministry of Munitions, and I resent your tone. If you will not accept my proposal I shall close the meeting. In that event I shall simply have an order for conversion issued by the Minister."

I inquired in a calm voice, "Before going into this order that you are simply having a Minister issue, I should like to know one thing—what people are going to run the place?"

"It goes without saying," Hettlage answered, "that the directors will come from the trustee firm. The choice will be a matter for agreement between Degenkolb's special committee and the trustee firm."

Just as I had thought. "Thank you. I understand now. I have one more question. What about the present directors and those in charge of all the research?"

"Whenever possible they will go on being employed in senior positions. Are you now ready to agree?"

"Professor," I snapped, "I haven't the slightest intention of agreeing. I am in no position to agree to anything of the kind. Peenemünde is an Army experimental station just like any other—Kummersdorf, for example, or Hillersleben, or even any simple drillground. Peenemünde is an Army command. In the armaments industry you may be able to put through any kind of reorganization you please, but you can never turn an Army command into a stock company. You might just as well try to turn an infantry regiment into one. In any case, you would need at the very least the consent of the Commander-in-Chief of the Home Front, Colonel General Fromm. My own opinion of your proposals can be stated very briefly. Do you really believe that after years of labor, with success just round the corner, I shall agree voluntarily to the change you plan and leave my closest associates, who were laughed to scorn for years, in the lurch? Never!"

Hettlage, Mackels, and Kunze stared at me in silence.

I continued, "Personal reasons apart, it will be impossible during the war to carry out your plan because the difficulties and loss of time would affect rocket development. I'll propose one to you instead. You may accept or decline it, just as you please. Come to Peenemünde and see the whole thing for yourself. You can thoroughly familiarize yourself with the whole organization, without my being there if you prefer. After that, if you can still see any feasible method of separating military and civilian interests without disturbance or friction I will gladly put your suggestions before Colonel General Fromm."

After beating about the bush for a time Hettlage accepted my invitation. Not long after, he came to Peenemünde. I had no idea how far I could trust the apparent agreement with my views which he expressed in my presence.

The first rift had appeared in my relations with Degenkolb. But he did not abandon the project and went on looking for new material until later events made his efforts pointless.

CHAPTER 9

HITLER'S PORTENTOUS DREAM

About a fortnight after Professor Hettlage's visit of exploration another professor, this time one Petersen, a director of AEG (General Electric Company), asked permission to look over Peenemünde on behalf of the Minister, Speer. I met him at the mess. Petersen was an old gentleman of middle height, wearing pince-nez, with iron-gray hair and a wrinkled, shriveled, sallow countenance. A permanent furrow at the corners of his mouth suggested conscious arrogance. The veins stood out conspicuously on his white, bony, old man's hands. He had a disagreeable way of talking, and his perpetual repetitions were constantly interrupted by a troublesome, nervous cough.

I asked what I could do for him. He said he had come on behalf of the Minister to make a thorough inspection of all the electrical components and equipment of our A-4. I handed him over to Steinhoff, and asked him to come and tell me, when he had finished his inspection, sincerely and frankly his impressions and opinions. The next day, before his departure, he had a meal with a select few of us in a private room in the mess. In reply to my words of farewell, he made a short speech.

"Colonel, gentlemen, now that my visit is over I can tell you that I, as a director of AEG, was sent here on the Führer's orders to make a responsible report of my impressions of the electrical side of your project. The question put to me was a simple one. Was there in fact any probability of the claims made by you ever being substantiated in practice? What possibility was there of employing the weapon in war, and with what degree of accuracy? What assistance could the German electrical industry give if necessary?

You have allowed me, Colonel, for two whole days to inspect anything I wished. I was permitted to consult every one of your colleagues. Nothing was kept secret. I was enabled to learn the methods and the ideas of you gentlemen. I must now admit that I have never seen before such a highly organized and expertly managed research station. The work done here under your supervision recalls the historic achievements of technology. I entered your establishment firmly determined to find ways and means of getting help for you from the German electrical industry. Now, after seeing the work you have done and the problems you have tackled, I shall ask you to help the German electrical industry! Thanks to perfectly equipped laboratories and experimental departments and to a great number of devoted engineers, you have, in several fields of work, but especially in high-frequency and guidance technique, forged years ahead of the technological stage reached by the German electrical industry. I should now like to thank you for the freedom of inspection accorded to me. I shall expressly state in my report that if the long-range rocket ever becomes a reality it can be produced only here and under your management."

After discounting the customary flattering exaggerations, enough was left over from this speech to make us feel proud and contented.

I never saw any report by Professor Petersen. A month later a "Long-Range Bombardment Development Commission" was set up within the Ministry of Munitions. This commission was to give ministerial direction to the development of all automatic or remote-controlled rocket missiles. It was composed of leading personalities from the Ministry, from heavy industry, from the Air Ministry, and from the staffs of the director of Army Ordnance and the Commander-in-Chief of the Reserve. A few representatives of firms collaborating in development were also included. The chairman of the commission was Professor Petersen!

The month of March 1943 was now approaching. Degenkolb with remarkable energy endeavored to get his organization into working order. His intention was to have three hundred A-4's produced monthly, starting from December 1943, in each of three factories, Peenemünde, the Zeppelin Works at Friedrichshafen, and the Rax Works at Wiener Neustadt. Journeys, conferences, and discussions went on interminably.

Degenkolb's working methods became evident. The man could not be induced to act within any particular terms of reference. For him, competent authorities, "channels," or any limitation of his scope did not exist. He negotiated over the heads of superiors with anyone he pleased and sent people wherever it suited him without the slightest regard for any work they might be doing at the time. Impulsive, hot-tempered, and presumptuous, he intervened brutally wherever he considered it necessary to do so, pulled all the strings he thought needed jerking for him to get his way, scrounged, dismissed, or interchanged executives without any special mandate on the strength of his position in the Ministry of Munitions. He dispensed insults, curses, and threats, and refused to go into detail. In his inordinate vanity and distrust of everyone, he was concerned only with keeping his reputation as an expert superior to any one else's. Consequently he drove even strong personalities to despair or resignation. Outstanding leaders of industry had to bend the knee before him, or take refuge in diplomatic trickery and deceit to avoid being ruined. He acted like a burly, endlessly threatening, and dreaded slave driver.

Degenkolb's system had proved successful in locomotive construction, an industry that had been neglected for years, though it remained perfectly efficient. In our case, however, production did not yet exist; no trained body of workers was available, much less any suitably qualified engineers. In addition, the different components of A-4, especially the electrical components, were considerably more diverse and complicated than those of any single locomotive, however large. Degenkolb's technical understanding was obviously inadequate to grasp the fact that we were dealing, not with sturdy objects like locomotives, but with extremely delicate mechanisms, such as potentiometers with tiny, hair-like wires known as "flies' legs." His mind was not subtle enough to understand such work.

The staff at Peenemünde was too small to make a start with production. The results of former neglect now began to show up. By this time reorganization and sheer drive could effect nothing. Degenkolb's methods had come too late and were bound to fail. He succeeded no better than we had in conjuring up, like lightning, allocations of raw materials, designers, and specialist engineers. What he needed was the very thing we old Peenemünde hands had been demanding from the outset—higher priorities.

His stubborn mind declined to recognize these facts. Since he lacked intuition, and also experience in our highly specialized scientific field, he made up for these deficiencies by an overbearing manner. He closed his mind to all demands and remonstrances, however justified they might be. He really believed that he would find solutions in time and could not see that we had no time left. He required blueprints for production that Peenemünde could not provide. His program was left in the air, for the foundations on which he intended to build were still utterly lacking. We had seen all these obstacles coming and had repeatedly called attention to their causes. We might just as well have talked to a stone wall. Disputes, reproaches, and general discord between my departments and Degenkolb were the result. A prey to corroding suspicions, the man snowed me under with complaints. We were due for wholesale catastrophe if he did not listen to what I had to say.

At last I realized that there was only one way to end the quarrel between Peenemünde and Degenkolb and his special committee. Degenkolb would have to be absorbed into the existing organization and place himself under my orders.

The Minister rejected this idea on grounds of principle. It was impossible for him, he said, to make any post in his Ministry subordinate to the command of an Army officer. Nor could he, on the other hand, appoint me his own representative and invest me with ministerial powers. Another eighteen months were to pass and the crisis was to become still more acute before Speer could bring himself to cast all such scruples to the winds. The only action he promised to take at once was to define in unmistakable terms, in conference, the relative positions of Degenkolb and myself.

Speer opened the meeting with the following address: "Gentlemen, I should like by way of introduction to define once and for all the position of Colonel Dornberger, as Army representative for the entire A-4 program, in relation to yourselves. If I, as architect and artist, think out, plan, and draw up a design for a certain building—the Chancellery, for instance—in all artistic and technical detail, and a builder who contracts to build, let us say, the Mosaics Room, independently decides to have whitewash walls instead of red marble, then, gentlemen, you must not think ill of me if I say that I have the right to punch his nose. The position of Colonel Dornberger in relation to yourselves is precisely the same as would be mine in relation to the builder."

I scarcely thought this elegant comparison would make much of an impression on Degenkolb. It was about as effective as using a pea shooter on a hippopotamus. Degenkolb recognized only people he had to fear. His position was still strong.

During the meeting Speer made up his mind to make another approach to Adolf Hitler. My hope rose again to some extent. This was March 1943, and work was already proceeding on the rocket bunker on the Channel coast.

A few days later the decisive message came from headquarters: "The Führer has dreamed that no A-4 will ever reach England."

Once more all had been in vain. Not only did we have to struggle with red tape and lack of vision in high places, but also, nowadays, with the dreams of our supreme warlord. Tension between Degenkolb on the one side and myself and my senior directors on the other increased. But slowly, though much too slowly, Degenkolb seemed to realize that without more technical personnel he could not get either production blueprints, designs for the tooling up of factories, or any other fundamental work. The more assembly shops he fitted up and the more factories he interested in the production of components, the more qualified engineers and expert craftsmen were needed at Peenemünde. At the beginning of May, Gauleiter Sauckel, the Führer's special commissioner for Labor Distribution, was invited to Peenemünde in the hope of persuading him to put further personnel at our disposal, but nothing came of his visit. On security grounds the employment of foreigners at Peenemünde was forbidden. German labor could not be allocated because of low priority. The building program was wrecked by the labor problem.

Degenkolb made the position still worse by withdrawing technicians from Peenemünde for service in his assembly works and underground oxygen-generating plants.

The state of affairs grew desperate.

CHAPTER 10

V-1 OR V-2 ?

Again a decisive hour struck for Peenemünde. Adolf Hitler decreed that to reduce the consumption of raw materials and cut down costs the Long-Range Bombardment Commission was to decide which of the two automatic long-range weapons had made the most progress and which had the best chance of success. An industrial committee was therefore to decide a purely military question.

About the middle of 1942 we rocket people had been exposed to competition. The Air Force, under the direction of Air Staff Engineer Brée, had with great rapidity developed a jet-driven air torpedo for catapulting from an inclined concrete ramp. It was called Model Fi-103. This missile, later known as the V-1, was basically a small, low-winged craft with a wing span of slightly over 25 feet. The propulsion system was said to be derived from an old French patent dating from the end of the previous century.

The power plant or rocket motor of our long-range rockets burned alcohol and oxygen. In Model Fi-103, low-grade fuel oil was mixed with oxygen from the air and ignited, thus creating a propulsive jet. This winged torpedo could fly only at uniform speed. It was therefore restricted for flight to a certain air density and consequently to a certain height, which, owing to the diminution of the oxygen content of the air at higher altitudes, could not be very great. Accordingly, its course corresponded to that of a small airplane and bore no comparison with that of a shell. The A-4 had continuous drive; in other words, the combustion process was uninterrupted during the whole period of burning. The air intake arrangement of the Fi-103 pulse jet engine, however, gave intermittent combustion with up to five hundred explosions per minute. Air was sucked in and compressed by means of a grid valve fitted to the duct head and provided with many rows of single flap plates opening inward. Fuel oil was injected into the compressed air and ignited. The resultant combustion pressure closed the valve flaps of the grid forward and forced the combustion gases and the air contained in the duct astern. This was accompanied by powerful expansion of the gases, and reaction propulsion took place. The expulsion of the air, however, led to strongly reduced pressure throughout the system, so that the valve flaps opened again, fresh air was sucked in, and the cycle was repeated. Such was the basic principle of the V-1 drive.

A miniature propeller fitted to the nose of the machine was connected with an adjustable revolution counter. The number of propeller revolutions was known for a given distance at uniform speed and height. On the arrival of the V-1 over the target the counter, set for that distance, switched on a release system which deflected the elevators. The missile then dived straight into the ground.

This invention seemed likely to succeed. The cost was about a tenth of that of our long-range rocket. The weight of the explosive carried was practically the same as in our A-4.

During the previous year we had witnessed, in the closest bonds of comradeship with Peenemünde West, the progress of the work. Ever since 1933 I had in my official capacity given enthusiastic financial support to development of the V-1 motor by Paul Schmidt, the Munich engineer. However, I was anxious to concentrate more on propulsion in practically airless space and therefore, in the spring of 1940, I had transferred the V-1 to the Air Ministry, which was more competent to deal with it. The jet drive which utilizes atmospheric oxygen is the ultumate in air-breathing engines designed to reach very high speeds inside the earth's atmosphere. Our own work, by contrast, lay in the wholly different realm of airless space. We were thinking in an entirely different system of measurements. We talked in terms of Mach numbers—that is, of multiples of the speed of sound—and referred to velocities in kilometers *per second* and not, as with aircraft, in kilometers *per hour*.

On May 26, 1943, the commission met in Peenemünde to study long-range bombardment. The highlight of the affair was to be a comparative demonstration of the two missiles to a large audience. Besides Speer, there were present Air Marshal Milch of the Luftwaffe, Admiral Dönitz, Colonel General Fromm, and a host of prominent personalities from Ministries and High Commands. Before the comparative tests the arguments for and against both weapons were debated in the mess. The model Fi-103 was considerably cheaper. Because of its moderate size it had the advantages of simplicity in handling, easy transportability on standard trucks, and low fuel consumption. These features made operational mass expenditure possible. The disadvantages were: first, big fixed launching sites liable to destruction by superior air power; second, the rigid line of fire imposed by the concrete ramp, which would make defense easier; third, the low speed of only 350 miles per hour, and the insufficient height of 600 to 6000 feet, making the Fi-103 vulnerable to fighters and light and medium antiaircraft; fourth, the characteristic sound of the pulse jet, which might warn the enemy. Moreover, the V-1 could easily be detected by radar. Because of its low speed of impact, its effect could not exceed that of a 1-ton land mine.

The A-4 rocket, on the other hand, could be freely launched in any direction from the motorized unit with little difficulty, and once launched there was no defense against it or possibility of interference with it. Spread of impact points, with proper servicing and testing before firing, was less than that of the Fi-103. Because of the high speed of impact the effect, if a sensitive proximity fuze was used, would be greater with the same load of high explosive. The impact would come as a complete surprise, owing to the supersonic impact velocity. The launching site itself would be difficult or impossible to identify from the air. Air attack, to be effective, would have to be restricted to the supply system. Location could be changed at any time at short notice. The disadvantages, in addition to higher costs, were vulnerable installations for testing and supply and the necessity for bomb-proof plants for liquid oxygen. Moreover, because the alcohol consumption of the A-4 was so high and available supply so low, the output would be fairly small. Finally, in view of the complexity and delicacy of the components of a self-steering rocket, spare parts would have to be available on a rather elaborate scale.

The commission concluded that the stage of development reached by the two weapons was practically the same.

During the discussion I took the position that in view of the difference in the two weapons and the tactical conditions of their employment there would be no point in favoring one at the expense of the other. The disadvantages of the one would be compensated by the other's advantages. But if at last it was really intended to make practical use of these long-range missiles, there had better be no limit to the strength deployed.

The commission decided to report to the Führer that the best solution would be to put both types into mass production as soon as possible with top priority and maximum output. To intensify the effect they should be used in conjunction.

This decision by the commission was reached before the comparative test firings, which would therefore not affect the report to Hitler.

That fine summer's day we were able to show two exemplary launchings of A-4's to a range of about 160 miles. Our competitors, owing to technical troubles, had bad luck with their model Fi-103. The machine crashed after a short flight. As we were leaving that afternoon, after yet another Fi-103 had failed, Air Marshal Milch clapped me on the back and observed with a rather wry grin, "Congratulations! Two-nothing in your favor!"

Later on, in the mess, I had the chance of a private chat with Speer. I did not shrink from remonstrating with him strongly for having abandoned his former attachment to Peenemünde and his faith in us since his appointment as Minister of Munitions.

"What was I to do?" Speer answered. "I was enthusiastic from the very first moment I had anything to do with this place. I've always admired the splendid vision of the Peenemünde projects and the big gamble you and your men were making. As you know, I've often closed both eyes to help you in the past. I was convinced you would succeed."

That was all very flattering, of course, but it didn't commit him to anything. I put another question, "Why then, sir, when you became Minister, did you not change the negative attitude of your Ministry and give us the help we asked so urgently time and again? We could have done what we demonstrated today eighteen months ago. All that time has been wasted, sir."

He tried to soothe me. "It's one thing to help you with what resources I have, when I'm Inspector General of Construction, carrying no responsibility for the conduct of the war, and quite another to do so as the minister responsible for German armaments, with a thorough knowledge of the multiple needs of the Armed Forces."

I could not quite bring myself to believe that. "If you had not doubted us yourself, sir," I protested, "you would surely have found some way of helping us."

Speer replied, "It's true that since being at the Ministry I have changed my opinion of your work and the possibility of your realizing your ideas. Is it to be wondered at? Right from the start, you know, I had to listen to the experts at the office. I'm sure that even you would have been shaken. Quite apart from the Führer's skeptical attitude, it was my own most important colleagues, technicians with great industrial experience, trained in development and production, who always regarded your plans with incredulity and doubt. I was up against defeatism, not once but at every turn. Whom was I to believe, when all's said and done? You, as a soldier, normally far removed from these things, or my Ministry's specialist engineers? Another thing, to us laymen the invention didn't look as if it was coming along very fast. I felt doubtful whether you would finish it before the war ended. I have full confidence now in the success of the scheme."

I had another question to ask.

"Why, sir, did you give me Degenkolb, of all people, to take charge of the special A-4 committee? It was only to be expected that disputes would arise, and it looks as if they will go on for-ever."

Speer replied that he had realized that Degenkolb, with his ruthlessness and primitive manners, would be most uncongenial to my colleagues and to me, but that it had been utterly impossible for him to obtain a higher priority for Peenemünde and that therefore the only solution had been Degenkolb's strong person-ality; the man had proved his ability in locomotive building.

"You just have to find some way of getting on together," Speer concluded.

"I shan't be able to stand him very much longer," I retorted.

"You'll have to get used to each other," Speer maintained. "The worst is over now—you've done the job and it's going ahead. I'll try to arrange for you to have an audience with the Führer as soon as possible. After that you can go on working to your heart's content. Then if you still find you really can't get along with Degenkolb, let me know and I'll relieve him."

The conversation was ended and I felt hopeful that produc-tion could now begin.

I was able to record yet another success for Peenemünde. On the way to the reception room I ran into Saur. He shook hands with me.

"I never knew, I never even dreamed you'd got so far! I see now that the rocket will be used after all. You have convinced me. From now on I shall be one hundred per cent behind you. I shall help you whenever I can. Come and see me if you want anything, either alone or with Degenkolb." And Saur actually kept his word.

After our guests had left I ended the day, as before, with a small party for my closest fellow workers.

Two days later Speer rang me up from headquarters to tell me that I had been promoted to major general.

CHAPTER 11

HITLER APPROVES

Once more Degenkolb was up to his dubious tricks. Four engineers whom he had sent turned up at Peenemünde. At once I began to hear extraordinary rumors. They caused me to telephone Degenkolb and ask what he had in mind. He explained that the four men were to familiarize themselves with the work so that later on they could serve as managers of his production lines. During a talk in my office I had further reason to suspect the honesty of Degenkolb's intentions. One of the engineers, Sawatski, told me confidentially that he and his colleagues had received from Degenkolb the clearest instructions to have a good look round at Peenemünde and send him, as soon as possible, proposals for reorganization. Nor were inducements to do so lacking. Degenkolb had assured all four that they were earmarked as future directors of the preproduction establishment. This was, of course, clear evidence that Degenkolb had not yet abandoned hope of transforming Peenemünde into a private company of his own. As he declined to recall his men, I sent them, except for Sawatski, back where they came from.

For the first time I sensed that all was too late. The demand for allocations of steel and building materials rose to incalculable heights, as did that for technical and building labor. It was the same story with vital equipment and machines. The shortage of specialist engineers became altogether too painful. Once again the situation was critical.

At last, on July 7, 1943, Hitler decided to give Peenemünde top priority in the German armaments program. The great struggle for recognition seemed to be over. Our situation began to improve by leaps and bounds. Manpower and materials streamed in. We accomplished in weeks what would have taken months and years. People fell over each other to give assistance. All ministries and authorities who were in the least concerned offered their support. We weren't even asked what our requirements were; the stuff was sent to us. Now that the decree had gone forth, people wanted to be "in on it." The pendulum had swung clear over.

On July 7 I was summoned, with von Braun and Steinhoff, to an audience at the Führer's headquarters. We started off in our Heinkel He-111 in a thick fog. Steinhoff was the pilot. The wireless operator kept calling airfields or meteorological stations on our route to find out how far the fog extended eastward. Our summons had come rather suddenly. At 11:30 I had had orders from Speer to report there and bring with me the film taken on October 3, 1942, together with any other useful material. How much time had gone by since October 3! Nearly nine months!

We had packed everything—the film, the model of the big firing bunker on the Channel coast, the little wooden models of vehicles, the colored sectional drawings, the organizational plans, the manual for field units, the trajectory curves.

I had not seen Hitler since March 1939. He had never visited Peenemünde. I could never account for this except on the grounds of fear of his own soldiers. Though he had not absolutely rejected our plans he had shown himself skeptical. He had never seen, even in a movie, the ascent of a long-range rocket, never experienced the thrill provided by the huge missile in flight, nor seen a place where one had hit the ground. So now we had to give him a convincing demonstration, in the lecture room, so to speak, of what we could do. We resolved to put on our usual program. First we would show the film of the October 3, 1942, test, accompanied by von Braun's commentary, which had now become a regular feature. Not until Hitler's interest had been keenly aroused and he had seen the inherent possibilities of the weapon from a moving picture would we touch upon other aspects.

As we flew over the Vistula, the fog ceased, as though cut away with a knife. Below us, as far as the eye could see, stretched the dark forests of East Prussia, plentifully adorned with sparkling lakes and occasional flower-decked meadows. Half an hour later we landed at Rastenburg. A headquarters staff car conveyed us and our bulky luggage to the Army Guest House, Hunter's Height. The first thing we heard there was that the lecture had been postponed. We were to attend at five o'clock that afternoon. I had expected something worse—cancellation.

An hour before the appointed time, armed with passes for the various prohibited areas, we drove into the clearing among oak trees where lay concealed the extensive barracks and concrete shelters of the Führer's headquarters. The projection room was in the innermost prohibited area. We hung up our plans there and arranged quite a little exhibition. Time went on, until it was long past five o'clock. It grew later and later.

Suddenly the door opened and we heard someone call out, "The Führer!" Hitler appeared in the company of Keitel, Jodl, Buhle, Speer, and their personal aides. No visitors were allowed. I was shocked at the change in Hitler. A voluminous black cape covered his bowed, hunched shoulders and bent back. He wore a field-gray tunic and black trousers. He looked a tired man. Only the eyes retained their life. Staring from a face grown unhealthily pallid from living in huts and shelters, they seemed to be all pupils.

After briefly greeting us he sat down between Speer and Keitel in the front row of the rising tiers of seats. After a few introductory remarks by me the place slowly grew dark.

Onto the screen came the historic ascent of the A-4 which had so enraptured us at the time and everyone who had seen it since. Von Braun gave his commentary. The shots were thrilling. The sliding gates, nearly a hundred feet high, of the great assembly hall of Test Stand VII opened. The heavy steel structure of the mobile test frame carrying, for a static test, a completely assembled A-4 rolled slowly out of the hall and over the great water-cooled blast tunnel sunk in the ground. Against the gigantic test scaffolding, resembling a house on wheels, the men in attendance shrank to nothing. Static tests followed, with the rocket suspended in gymbals. Close-ups of the mechanism of the jet vanes were shown. After the static test the rocket was loaded onto a Meiller-wagen, the transporter scheduled for field use. Driving tests on straight and curved roads proved the remarkable ease with which the rocket could be carried.

Soldiers operating the hydraulic "erector" set the rocket verti-cally on the launching table, so astonishingly simple in design. The Meillerwagen's hydraulic machinery handled the 46-foot rocket weighing 4.5 tons like a toy. Sequences showing fueling procedure and preparations for launching proved the missile capable of use under field conditions. Finally came the actual launching. Extreme close-ups showed the process of take-off and the vertical ascent of the rocket, then the tilting movement into the line of fire. In conclusion, various processes were shown in slow motion.

This photographic documentation was followed by animated cartoons of the trajectory of the shot, indicating speeds, heights, and range reached that day.

The last few feet of the film exhibited the key events of the whole operation in rapid succession—the arrival of the crew at the test stand, static tests, work in the drafting room, and finally the launching itself. The end of the film was announced by a sen-tence which filled the entire screen:

"We made it after all!"

That was the finish. Von Braun ceased speaking. Silence. No one dared utter a word.

Hitler was visibly moved and agitated. Lost in thought, he lay back in his chair, staring gloomily in front of him. When, after a while, I began to enter into some lengthy explanations he came to with a start and listened attentively. He showed real interest. It was as if he were reading the words from my face and lips before I uttered them. At times he shook his head or nodded eager agree-ment.

I summed up again briefly the current stage of development. I stated how the weapon could be employed and what preparations were necessary. I then explained the procedure for firing from the large bunker and from motorized batteries. From the subject of industrial planning, for which I gave output figures and delivery dates, I turned to the question of launching crews, their formation and training. I tried to give an impressive picture, with the aid of our models, drawings, and maps, of the development work which had kept us breathlessly occupied for years.

During my speech Hitler jumped up and crossed over to the table on which we had arranged our little show of models. His glance darted incessantly between me and the objects on view. At last there was nothing more to say. I stopped speaking and waited for questions.

Hitler came over and shook my hand. He said in a whisper, "I thank you. Why was it I could not believe in the success of your work? If we had had these rockets in 1939 we should never have had this war . . ." His gaze seemed to lose itself in space and he stopped looking at me. His lips alone moved. "Europe and the world will be too small from now on to contain a war. With such weapons humanity will be unable to endure it."

He turned again to the model of the bunker. We had to take it all to pieces again and explain everything a second time. We had to show him how the rockets could be brought up, stored, tested, and got ready for launching; then how, after being set up, they could be moved through the narrow sliding doors into the open, one minute before firing, with their interior gyroscopes running, and then launched almost immediately from their vertical position on the table.

I made no secret of my dislike of firing from the bunker. My preference is for maneuverability, for profiting from motorization, for quick fieldwork and firing on the move. If an enemy was greatly superior in the air, there wouldn't be much shooting from a bunker.

Hitler interrupted me impulsively and called Speer over to tell him that it was these same large-scale bunkers on the Channel coast that had proved so useful for submarines. He wanted to have not one but two or if possible three bunkers put up for us.

Motorized rocket batteries, in his opinion, would soon be spotted by enemy reconnaissance and engaged. The future was to prove him wrong.

Although I knew that Hitler could not stand contradiction I did not hesitate to contest his view. I observed that if a mobile battery was used, it would be extremely difficult for an aircraft, after a rocket had been launched, to identify the launching site. Only the small firing table would be left behind, with a few vehicles which it would be child's play to camouflage. It would be no trouble to change location after each round, and no target worth bombing would remain to tell the tale.

My arguments were in vain. Bunkers were Hitler's favorite buildings and he would not drop the idea. Speer received orders to have the roof of the bunker built to a thickness of 23 feet. Hitler added this explanation of the plan, "These shelters must lure the enemy airmen like flies to a honeypot. Every bomb that drops on them will mean one less for Germany."

After I had shown him two photographs of rocket craters on land he asked, after examining them for some time in silence, whether we could not raise the load of explosive to 10 tons and the monthly deliveries to two thousand. I replied that an entirely new rocket of enormously larger size would be needed and that if the range was to be maintained such charges could not be handled with current resources. It would take at least four or five years to develop such a gigantic rocket.

"What about quantities?" Hitler interposed impatiently.

"Not possible either," I explained. "We haven't enough alcohol. The figures mentioned in my lecture are the highest that the planning offices would authorize. Any alternative propellant of different origin and composition," I added, "would also mean a new rocket and could not be ready for some years."

A strange, fanatical light flared up in Hitler's eyes. I feared he was going to break out into one of his mad rages.

"But what I want is annihilation—annihilating effect!"

How could I answer that obstinately bawled demand? Speer, Keitel, Jodl, Buhle, and the others stood silent and apart, watching me closely. I replied briefly, "No one can get more out of a ton of explosive than it is capable of giving. We might be able to increase the effect to some extent by using a particularly sensitive fuze. We have not yet tested that, nor has any expert so far been able to prove it theoretically."

Hitler turned again to the models. I went on speaking to his profile. I guessed his thoughts.

"Please discourage the propaganda that is starting about the decisive effect these 'all-annihilating wonder weapons' are going to have on the war," I urged. "It can lead to nothing but disappointment for the populace. Our aim was to increase the range of heavy artillery out of all recognition by using new methods. We have succeeded. We have also, by the use of rockets, reduced to a minimum the inadmissible weight of super-heavy guns in the field. With a spread that is quite reasonably low we can fire about a ton of explosive a hundred and sixty miles and cover targets only bombers could reach before, without risking a machine or a crew. No defense against the rocket exists . . ."

As Hitler said nothing and continued to listen attentively I went on with particular emphasis, "We have developed this weapon. We can service it and put it to tactical use. It was not our task to assess its psychological effect, its usefulness in present conditions, or its strategic importance in the general picture."

While I was talking I suddenly realized with absolute certainty that Hitler, after all these years of hesitation, now expected the new weapon to produce a decisive turning point in the war. The 10-ton payload he had demanded a few minutes before was evidence of the fact. But even that senseless demand, assuming it could be met, would not decide the war. For that we needed new means of destruction, new sources of energy. Would it be atomic energy? Out of the question. I knew how slight was the progress made in that field in recent years by the Research Branch of the Army Weapons Department. I knew how seriously the whole project had been upset by the destruction of the heavy-water plant in Norway. It would take years to get provisional results, even assuming the highest degree of priority and maximum resources.

As sober engineers designing our first rocket in 1936, we had not dreamed of such remote possibilities. I felt I must try again to make clear to him what he might fairly expect. Wishful thinking would get us nowhere. So I began once more, "When we started our development work we were not thinking of an all-annihilating effect. We—"

Hitler swung round in a rage and shouted at me, "You! No, *you* didn't think of it, I know. But *I* did!"

In the face of this outburst I decided to keep silent. Keitel hastened to change the subject by stressing the need for more air-raid defenses at Peenemünde. Antiaircraft guns were granted forthwith. The tension relaxed.

Hitler promised, as proof of his favor, that from now on we should enjoy top priority.

CHAPTER 12

A NIGHT AT THE FÜHRER'S HEADQUARTERS

The strangest moment of all, however, was to come. I had walked a little apart, leaving von Braun to explain some technical points to Hitler. Meanwhile I reminded Speer of his promise made me at Peenemünde to propose a titular professorship for von Braun. As Hitler, after some general conversation, took his leave he congratulated von Braun on his nomination to that title. But before the Führer left the room, and when he was already halfway to the door, he suddenly turned round and walked back to me. The words I was now to hear I regarded as the fatefully ironic climax of all our labors up to that time, including all intrigues and other afflictions.

"I have had to apologize to only two men in my life. The first is Field Marshal von Brauchitsch. I did not listen to him when he told me again and again how important your research was. The second man is yourself. I never believed that your work would be successful."

He walked out of the room with his aides. We were left alone.

I could not feel happy about it all. I saw myself exposed to the dangerously dynamic personality of this unpredictable man, with his possibly exaggerated hopes. Was he not expecting too much, at this stage, of our rockets? We had not in fact created any weapon that would put a quick end to the war. That had not been our aim, nor would it have lain in our power. Von Braun and I had already been uneasy on this point during our flight to Rastenburg. We had been annoyed by the propaganda. The catchword was "wonder weapons," and wherever we went it was obvious that the phrase was giving rise to exaggerated hopes. Apart from that, our A-4, the long-range missile with the simple workshop name "Aggregate No. 4," had been turned into a V-2, standing for "Vengeance Weapon No. 2"! We had not exaggerated our claims in front of Hitler. Von Braun had repeatedly begged me during the flight to stress the limitations of what we could do.

In sum, what was the V-2? It was by no means a "wonder weapon." This term was in itself an exaggeration which did not correspond with the facts. By the middle of 1943 the military situation had long ceased to be such that by launching nine hundred V-2's a month, each loaded with a ton of explosive, over ranges of 160 miles, one could end the Second World War.

I was haunted by forebodings.

That evening we were entertained by Speer in the very simply and tastefully furnished tea house at the headquarters. Other guests were Funk, Economics Minister; Backe, Minister of Food; Pleiger, the coal dictator; Dr. Morell, Hitler's physician; Dr. Brand, and a few members of Hitler's personal staff.

Hitler, as always in recent months, ate alone.

We had soup, fish, and pudding, with a glass of wine. Conversation at table was sustained mainly by Funk and Pleiger, who vied with one another in telling Rhineland and Hamburg jokes. We held our tongues.

After the meal we had coffee, brandy, Steinhäger, and cigars in the adjoining room, sitting in comfortable armchairs. Conversation in the smoke-filled room was gradually dominated by an excited debate between Speer and Funk. Speer was perfectly sober and his coolness gave him the advantage. I was astonished and interested to hear how a battle of power politics that had been raging for months between the Economics and Munitions ministries was settled in that alcohol-laden atmosphere in Speer's favor. Finally Funk, very tipsy, went to sleep in his corner.

But there was a further ordeal in store for the Economics

Minister. He had been due for a late-afternoon audience with Hitler. The appointment had been put off from hour to hour. Hitler was working, or in conference, or asleep for a while, or in conference again, or again asleep. One had to be ready for him at any hour of the day or night.

Finally, at four o'clock in the morning, Funk was sent for. He was waked up and given strong black coffee to put him on his feet. He regained his senses amazingly quickly. After half an hour he returned, perfectly sober and in full command of his faculties. But shortly afterward he fell asleep again.

Meanwhile a fresh disturbance had arisen. Pleiger found fault with our presence. He declared we had no business to be there. At last he asked Speer, with a glance at von Braun and Steinhoff, "What on earth are these young foot-sloggers doing here?"

Speer winked at me and answered, "Oh, they were with the Führer this evening, putting up an idea about a new rocket invention."

Pleiger was most astonished and indignant. "Putting up an idea about rockets! What do they mean by it? I'm the man in charge of rocket development in Germany. If these boys want to get anywhere they'd better come to me!" So here was another fellow who owned German rocket development!

"That won't be so easy," Speer responded with a smile. "The General here would like to have them himself."

Pleiger blustered. "Rubbish! There'll be nothing but office jobs there for them. Send them to me!"

"Better ask the General," Speer advised him amusedly. "He might let them go."

Speer and I now indulged in a little leg-pulling at the expense of this noisy, self-satisfied Westphalian. To lead him on, I said to Pleiger, "Are you sure you would pay the salary they ask? They are both qualified engineers. They've just left Technical College and are starting out. I believe they've got some ideas. If you could guarantee them steady work and the pay they want, I might be persuaded. Salaries are a perpetual headache for me. How about making me an offer?"

Pleiger asked what they would want. I mentioned 250 marks a month, to begin with.

That nocturnal conversation between Pleiger and myself led to a long correspondence. Pleiger actually signed an employment contract and sent it to Peenemünde. In the end, after consulting Speer, I put an end to the joke, went to see Pleiger and made a clean breast of it. Naturally he lost his temper at first. But I managed to calm him by suggesting that he should pretend he had known everything from the start but simply not wanted to spoil our little game.

I have told this insignificant little story only to show how well Peenemünde's secret was kept as late as the middle of 1943. None of the people in that conversation at the Führer's head-quarters, except Speer, had any idea that long-range rocket development was going on in Germany at all.

At seven in the morning we drove back at last to the guest house. At eight-thirty we started our return journey to Peene-münde. We flew across Swinemünde Bay and crossed the coast over Zinnowitz at a great height. Once more—and for the last time—I was delighted with the view of Peenemünde from the air and the vast extent and magnificence of the Army and Air Force establishments hidden in its forest solitudes.

Next time I saw the buildings from the air the picture had fundamentally changed. Then smoke clouds were rising from burning buildings, and the forest was on fire—results of the heavy air raid in which Peenemünde received its first direct hit.

I had had forebodings, and they had not misled me. At the beginning of July 1943 Saur, head of the Central Office at the Ministry of Munitions, invited the managers of the larger concerns included in our works program, together with their senior technicians and the chairmen of the Labor Commissions dealing with the program, to a big meeting in the conference room of the Ministry, then in barracks at the Zoo.

As I entered and sat down on Saur's left at the ministerial table the big room resounded to the hubbub of two hundred and fifty people all talking excitedly at once. A few moments before, Saur had announced the extension he planned of the Degenkolb program, raising production from nine hundred to two thousand units a month, beginning with December.

The meeting was not yet officially opened. Degenkolb, beaming, shook hands with me. Professor von Braun, seated on my left at a long table, was giving me imploring and despairing looks, shaking his head again and again in incredulous astonishment. Who had given Saur that crazy idea, I wondered. Had the new program been arranged privately between him and Degenkolb?

I soon realized what the basic calculation was. Three hundred units were to have been produced monthly in each of three factories already earmarked for some time. To this original figure had been added the expected output of nine hundred a month planned for the Nordhausen Mittelwerk, a new emergency factory still under construction, and the total simply was rounded off.

Two factors made this program impossible: lack of both ground installations and fuel. I at once tried to make this clear to Saur. The equipment the mobile batteries needed could not be speeded up. Underground oxygen-generating plants could not be conjured up from nowhere. How much alcohol we should have depended on the potato harvest. Fuel could not be fully guaranteed even for nine hundred units a month.

My arguments were in vain. In my anger at this lack of understanding I was minded to leave the meeting. With an effort I kept my self-control and stayed. At least I wanted to know how industry was going to respond to this impossible target. I had known only Degenkolb's methods up to now and had never attended so large a meeting as this at the Ministry of Munitions.

At last the meeting was declared open. Degenkolb took the chair; Saur supported him at decisive points.

Saur began with a tribute to my colleagues and myself. He described his early doubts about our work and his later conversion. He announced that he was now prepared to support us with all the means at the disposal of the Ministry of Munitions. Adolf Hitler's decision, the importance of the project, and the need to strain every nerve to achieve success were the main topics of his address. He ended by calling upon me, as head of Peenemünde and representative of the Armed Forces, to say a few words.

I took the opportunity to describe the difficulties in the way of production and ended my speech with these words: "Gentlemen, you know now what stoppages may occur if the quality of the components you supply is not up to standard. I am opposed to intoxication with figures. Better fewer rockets of first-rate quality than masses of inferior ones that cannot be used except as scrap. Most earnestly I request you to base your estimates of deliveries at the appointed dates strictly on the best quality that you can guarantee."

My voice died away in a vacuum. It was as though I had not spoken.

The meeting proceeded to discuss details. Degenkolb took the floor. He said, "We now come to the question of fuel. Herr Heyland, can you deliver the required quantities of liquid-oxygen apparatus?"

Heyland stood up. He tried in vain to speak with firmness. "I have several times explained to you the difficulties that stand in the way of meeting this schedule," he began.

Degenkolb interrupted. "I am not interested in your difficulties. My question was whether you could deliver the required machinery by the dates named."

Heyland turned distractedly to his technicians and conferred with them.

Saur at once lost patience. He stood up and called out sharply down the room, "You have been asked a question, Herr Heyland."

Heyland straightened up and replied in a steady tone, "I can only repeat that if I am given my steel vouchers in time and if the subcontractors—"

This time it was Saur who interrupted him. "What schedule are you talking about?"

"The Degenkolb schedule," Heyland replied in astonishment.

Saur retorted sharply, "Don't you realize that as from this morning there is no such thing as a Degenkolb schedule? My schedule is now the only one and it requires two thousand units a month."

"Before I give my views I must consult my technical staff," Heyland answered in an effort to gain time.

Saur cut him short. "Either you are the responsible leader of the Heyland Company and know what is going on, or you are not fit to be a business leader. If so I shall have to dismiss you from your position with immediate effect and reserve the right to have your business conducted in future by some suitable trustee. I have no more to say to you. Degenkolb, call the next firm!"

Every industrialist who did not agree without qualification met the same fate. The consequence was that opposition and objections grew weaker and weaker until finally the heads of firms, when asked whether they could meet the schedule, merely nodded resignedly.

Was it lack of civic courage, of a sense of responsibility? Probably all the industrialists were so completely convinced of the impossibility of meeting Saur's schedule that they believed there would be no harm in agreeing, since the program would come to grief anyhow. Everyone naturally hoped that someone else would be the first to confess failure. They hoped that they might thus gain time. Obviously each individual business would try to do its best. But I knew that not one would succeed in carrying out the program.

What Saur and Degenkolb were trying to achieve by these methods was evident enough to me. They were trying, by putting the screws on industry, to extract the possible maximum output.

I left the conference room with von Braun, in a state of intense despair.

Air raids on Peenemünde on August 17, 1943, and on the Zeppelin Works at Friedrichshafen and the Rax Works at Wiener Neustadt, wrecked the Saur program shortly afterward. *Force majeure!* The Degenkolb program again became the order of the day.

CHAPTER 13

PEENEMÜNDE AT WORK

A typical day at Peenemünde went something like this:

Dr. Hermann asked me to come and see him as he had something to show me. I ordered my car to call for me at 10:30 at the building which housed the supersonic wind tunnel, and as the working day began walked the few hundred yards from the administration building of the Army Experimental Station, out through the inner gate, past the Materials Test Building and the Tool Workshop, to a long, low, building of red brick. This was the show piece of our establishment both artistically and functionally. The high central block of the building gave it character. It stood in well-kept gardens among tall pines. I walked across the wide, bright entrance hall and entered the reception room, where Dr. Hermann was waiting for me beneath a quotation engraved in the wall: "Technologists, physicists, and engineers are among the pioneers of this world."

This slender young scientist, exceptionally conscientious, experienced, and knowledgeable, had a long head with a lofty brow and light-brown, wavy hair brushed straight back. He had shrewd eyes and used expressive gestures. He was in charge of our unique supersonic wind tunnel and was its guiding spirit. He had taken the leading part in its design and construction. The tunnel had been in operation since November 1939. For years now the characteristic shrill hiss of air streaming at high speed through the measuring section had been mingling with the roar of rocket motors that filled the woods of Peenemünde.

For months the wind tunnel had been worked in two or even three shifts, at an average of 500 wind-tunnel hours per month.

Work hours ran from 7 in the morning until 2 at night. There were two alternately used measurement sections. Outside air was sucked in through large funnels, passed through drying filters, sent through sheet-metal straighteners in the tunnel which smoothed the air-flow, and then accelerated to the supersonic speed which corresponded to the Laval nozzle in use. In a perfectly parallel flow, without any turbulence and with equal pressure at every point, the air passed around the model of the rocket suspended in the measurement section. This enabled us to ascertain the aerodynamic forces created at the given speed of airflow. The pressure in the measurement section was adjusted and kept constant for the duration of the test by means of a variable diffuser which changed the cross-sectional area.

The outside air was sucked into a large spherical vacuum chamber through an expanding section with a quick-action shutter which could be instantly closed at the end of a test. Before the beginning of a test this vacuum chamber was deprived of 98 per cent of its air by means of three twin-pump assemblies with a total power of 1000 horsepower. The vacuum chamber had a capacity of 35,000 cubic feet, its diameter was 41 feet, and the wall thickness 0.67 inches. The wind tunnel was open at one end and worked intermittently. Between tests, which lasted about 20 seconds, there had to be a pause of from 3 to 5 minutes until the vacuum had been restored.

In planning the Peenemünde establishment I had not wanted a tunnel for basic aerodynamic research, nor an experimental wind tunnel, but one for a specific purpose. It was to establish, in the shortest possible time, the necessary data—based on thorough and prolonged series of tests—for a number of projectile and missile shapes which were already under development. In order to carry out these tests some basic research had to be done too and I had allotted 30 per cent of the tunnel time for this purpose. From the very beginning I had stipulated, however, that the reports sent by the wind-tunnel men to designers, trajectory computers, and those dealing with control equipment should be intelligible to people who were not professional aerodynamicists.

I was not impressed by overingenious treatises or arguments unintelligible to the ordinary mortal and overburdened with figures. We did not wish to set the scientific world on fire. We needed data for our work. We didn't bother so much about the "why" as about the "how," which in any case was decisive in wartime. The theories which emerged from such reports could not concern us except superficially. What we needed were clearly expounded facts.

The wind-tunnel establishment, like the rest at Peenemünde, was organized to suit the personalities of the scientists in charge. I expected the man in charge to bear the whole responsibility. He had to run his department administratively as well as scientifically in consultation with his colleagues. Thus we achieved the results we needed by the collective work of all the men engaged in a given field, properly influenced and directed by the man in charge. Heads of departments who merely lent their names to the work did not last long.

I walked with Dr. Hermann through the soundproof corridor that separated the pumps, the great vacuum chamber, and the measurement section from the design and administrative offices, and entered the actual test room. There I was met by Dr. Kurzweg, in charge of research, Chief Engineer Gessner, constructor of the wind tunnel, the balances, and models, and Engineer Ramm, who dealt with the development of all measuring equipment.

Dr. Hermann wished to show me the stability characteristics of a new model of the A-9 pattern, an A-4 with wings, at a Mach number of 4.4—that is, a velocity 4.4 times the speed of sound, or nearly 3500 miles per hour.

I walked under the first of the measurement sections accompanied by Dr. Hermann, until we came face to face with the thick parallel panes of plate glass, which gave a view of the Laval nozzle and the measurement chamber and enclosed the chamber on both sides.

On our side the plate glass had been pushed back. The air stream leaving the Laval nozzle measured 16 by 16 inches in cross section. In a rhombus-shaped space, the size of which depended on wind velocity (that is, the length of its sides was determined by the reflection of the shock waves developed at supersonic speed), the air stream was closely similar to that around an actual body flying through open atmosphere. It was only in this space that the measurements essential for our work could be taken. It contained the suspended model, rotatable on an axis running through its center of gravity—a small missile resembling the A-4 in shape but with two knifelike, very thin, swept-back wings. The model rotated at the slightest touch. Dr. Hermann now closed the inner glass pane which formed one side wall of the Laval nozzle, then the outer one, so that the measurement chamber was completely shut in. Our intention today was to take oscillation measurements and see whether the model, the shape of its wings having been determined in the wind tunnel, would be stable at this high supersonic speed—that is, whether it would turn its nose into the airflow representing the direction of flight, and also whether its oscillations about that course would fade after a few vibrations and thus prove that it also possessed the necessary aerodynamic damping capacity.

Our measuring equipment and Laval nozzles had been developed in the first troublesome and toil-filled year after completion of the wind tunnel. At that time we had constructed the first three-component balance, which gave us the essential equipment of drag, lift, and lateral coefficients. By the end of 1940 we had a set of nozzles which gave speeds corresponding to Mach numbers 1.2 to 4.4. Our work was also considerably lightened by the fact that changing nozzles now took only from 10 to 15 minutes.

Since the accuracy of the three-component balance was insufficient for taking measurements on guided missiles, we developed devices for taking oscillation measurements on freely vibrating models. Evaluation of these vibrations, taken on oscillograms, enabled us to determine the center of pressure which would be decisive for stabilization, and to ascertain lift and aerodynamic damping.

In addition, we constructed, inside the model, built-in balances for determining roll moments and stability.

With models of missiles earmarked for final development, like the A-4, the A-9, and the antiaircraft rocket *Wasserfall*, pressure distribution measurements were carried out at a great variety of speeds and angles of attack. The models, 1.5 to 2.0 inches wide and 12 to 16 inches long, were for this purpose halved along their longitudinal axes and mounted on plates. The pressure changes were then simultaneously measured at as many as one hundred and ten different points over the body, wings, and tail fins of this small model. This method of measurement was gradually improved until a model could be thoroughly measured, twice over, at all Mach numbers and angles of attack by a double shift, each of thirty-five men, in a period of fourteen days. The designer thus obtained guiding principles for his work.

The shape and effectiveness of the vanes were ascertained by measurements of their moments. Measurements of the expansion of the rocket blast at great heights provided data about the shape to be given to the stabilizing surfaces. Investigations of the influence of the jet on stability and drag of the A-4 established that at subsonic speed the drag coefficient rose by 70 per cent and the center of pressure slipped back half a caliber length, or one missile radius. At supersonic speed, on the other hand, the drag coefficient dropped as much as 30 per cent.

For all these investigations special measuring equipment had to be developed.

Dr. Hermann now began to explain the stability tests he wished to carry out for us.

"One of the main requirements of rocket construction is that missiles shall be sufficiently but not excessively stable throughout the range covered by the speed and angle of attack. The greater the stability, the greater must also be the moment to be applied, which means both larger vane surface and a more powerful servo-mechanism."

I confirmed his statement. "Quite right, Doctor. The laws of rocket flight can't be outwitted. The maximum flying speed of a rocket is, of course, directly dependent on the exhaust velocity of the gases and the ratio between its take-off mass and remaining mass. We must therefore keep the empty weight as low as we can. Demands on the servomechanism must be reduced as much as possible."

"That's why I think it should be my business," continued Dr. Hermann, "to give the rocket an aerodynamic form that would permit guidance with the least possible vane surface and the smallest possible servomechanism. With the remote-controlled antiaircraft rocket this is actually a matter of life and death. In comparison the coefficient of drag is of secondary importance. The main point is that the location of the center of pressure be kept constant as far as possible for all angles of attack and through the whole speed range from zero through the speed of sound to supersonic speeds. As you know, sir, this condition was met, in the case of the Wasserfall, after extensive research in our tunnel, by a proper shaping and arrangement of wings and tail surfaces."

"Exactly," I agreed. "And today, Doctor, I should like to see what you have accomplished with the A-9."

He pressed a button, and the Schlieren apparatus, which renders differences in air density visible, rolled along a 10-yard rail to cover the measuring section. The rocket model and its support were clearly silhouetted on the screen of the instrument. While this was going on, I remembered a question I had meant to ask Dr. Hermann.

"How did the experiments on the feasibility of an acoustic proximity fuze turn out? It's about time we gave short shrift to those doubting Thomases who insist that a body moving at supersonic speed cannot receive normal sound waves."

"The experiments were successful. The shock waves occurring at supersonic speed do not stop the sound waves from getting through provided the sensing instrument has been properly shaped."

"How was the experiment arranged?"

"We had the receiver microphone in the nose of the model and at Ramm's suggestion we built into a slit round the head a fine-meshed, circular wire grid in several layers. The supersonic flow went smoothly and undisturbed over this grid, without 'specific noise,' that is, without creating its own intrusive sound waves, as all other receiver heads had done. The sound waves of the siren operating in the intake funnel of the measurement section went through the shock waves at Mach numbers 1.22 to 4.4 without interruption in a perfectly audible frequency range."

"Good! Then there can't possibly be any more doubt about the matter. When do I get the reports? The Antiaircraft Section of the Air Ministry keeps on asking me about the results."

"In a few days, I hope."

Meanwhile the preparations had come to an end and we could get going. The silhouette of the missile rose clearly before us, the nose pointing almost straight upward, against the bright background of the screen, which resembled a luminous vapor bath.

The Schlieren equipment had been built by Zeiss of Jena after protracted experiments undertaken in the wind tunnel. The equipment had already done yeoman service for us and proved the best of all our measurement devices to date. All differences in air density caused by pressure or heat showed up on the screen as bright or dark lines. Countless experiments and measurements concerned with the thickness and location of the boundary layer, its detachment, the structure, direction, and behavior of the shock waves, the expansion of the exhaust after leaving the nozzle at great heights, and so on, had been carried out with this apparatus.

A test engineer now pressed the button that caused the quick-acting shutter to open; the air raced hissing through the measuring section into the vacuum sphere.

The model moved abruptly, turning its nose into the oncoming airstream. After a few quickly damping oscillations of slight amplitude it lay quiet and stable in the air that hissed past it at 4.4 times the speed of sound. At the nose, and at the edges of the wing supports and guide mechanism, the shock waves could be clearly seen as they traveled diagonally backward at a sharp angle and sent their characteristic lines of different degrees of brightness across the black-and-white picture. The boundary layer enveloping the missile showed bright above and darker below the model, in clear relief. It could be seen pulling back and tending to detach itself as it broadened over the tapering stern section.

Twenty seconds passed, which seemed interminable. Then the picture changed abruptly. The test engineer closed the quick-acting valve. The distinct lines in the picture grew blurred, their angles opened, they moved forward, and a sort of eddy occurred. Then they vanished completely. Smoke seemed to be rising in the bright background of the screen. The model was no longer lying in a stable position. It made a few turns about its center of gravity, then it came to a standstill with the nose pointing downward. The experiment Dr. Hermann had wished to show me had succeeded perfectly. This projectile, shaped like an airplane, had remained absolutely stable at a supersonic speed range of almost 3500 miles per hour.

"Excellent, Doctor," I approved. "That was all as it should be. What about the fly in the ointment?"

"I've been trying, by using all sorts of wing configurations— swept-back, delta, straight, rectangular, low- and high-aspect ratios —to make the missile stable and controllable at all speeds, as well as to keep an acceptable relation between lift and drag; in other words, to give it a good Lift/Drag ratio. But so far we haven't quite been able to manage it."

"Do you think that you'll be able to do it?"

"Yes. The trouble is that we are limited by specifications. We are supposed to keep the body of the A-4 and are only permitted to add wings and change the external vanes in the tail surfaces. This handicaps us considerably. The high-lift swept-back wings do produce the best L/D ratio, but just below the speed of sound, with angles of attack between plus and minus two degrees, the stability is insufficient."

"Why is that?"

"The tail surfaces lie in the turbulent wake of the wings. Furthermore, the swept-back wing has the disadvantage that a relatively large shift of the center of pressure occurs between subsonic and supersonic speed. We could have fixed that all right if we had not also been told to keep the present control and stabilizing surfaces for the A-9. Still, I hope we shall soon be able to find a solution."

"How would you propose to avoid the turbulent wake of the wings? I am sorry that my proposal to merge the trailing edge of the wings with the leading edges of the tail surfaces did not prove too successful."

"Lift was too small with that arrangement. So we tried once more to raise the L/D ratio by means of 'steps,' which proved so useful in the case of the tail fins. But even that didn't quite work. The L/D ratio improved by twelve per cent but still remained twelve per cent worse than with the swept-back wing. That means a loss of range of nearly forty miles."

"Well, try it again with the trapezoidal wing. If we managed to avoid shift of the center of pressure in the case of the antiaircraft rocket, shouldn't we succeed in this case, too? Good stability and control are the main things, and in my opinion they would be worth a certain sacrifice in the L/D ratio."

Dr. Hermann looked thoughtful and glanced at me rather dubiously. I had to laugh.

"My dear Doctor, if I had, like you, got an aircraft model to remain stable at a speed of over thirty-five hundred miles per hour I would be very happy."

While the tests were proceeding Gessner asked me to look at his new designs for the Peenemünde "arrow projectile." I still had five minutes to spare before going to Test Stand VII, where a static test with the A-4 was going to take place at 10:30.

Gessner took me over to his drawing boards and calculations. His work on arrow projectiles derived from my suggestion that it might be possible to increase artillery range without altering existing gun design. This was why I had asked Dr. Hermann to make subcaliber fin-stabilized projectiles, which could be fired from ordinary gun barrels, and get them tested in the wind tunnel.

Gessner had applied himself with much zeal and success to the structural studies required. To achieve stabilization of these extremely slender, narrow-finned projectiles of very low air resistance and at speeds of 3000 to 3500 miles per hour, innumerable tests were carried out in the wind tunnel. The drag of the arrow-type projectile was lowered to 35 per cent of the resistance of a normal shell. This laid the foundation for a considerable increase in range. Though naturally ridiculed and snubbed at first by the Ballistic and Munitions Division, the competent authority in this matter, we had now succeeded very well indeed with our Peenemünde arrow-type projectiles.

Gessner developed projectiles for the 105-millimeter antiaircraft gun and the heavy 280-millimeter K-5, which had a range of 37 miles. With an arrow-type projectile, the powder gases of which, when the gun was fired, acted upon a sabot behind the thick-walled fins, range could be increased to 56 miles with the same weight of steel and a reduction of the high-explosive charge by only 13 pounds. With a new, lighter type of shell, which instead of a sabot had an obturation skirt attached to its middle, we actually reached 85 to 93 miles. This feat broke all existing records of projectile ballistics. Lateral dispersion amounted only to about 2 mils, thus improving on the K-5. Dispersion in range, however, was still nearly twice that of the ordinary shell. Certain functional trouble still existed, which would undoubtedly be ended with further development.

The research thus started in pure aerodynamics was capable of giving weapon development new directions, and of increasing, in association with projectile designers and experts in ballistics, the range of artillery.

I now really had to go. Had I been tempted to accompany Dr. Hermann to his office and discuss the newly completed model of the great Mach number 10 tunnel, with a working cross section of 3 by 3 feet, I should not have been able to get away in a hurry. As early as December 1941, we had embarked on the project of a super-supersonic tunnel, for a speed ten times that of sound, in connection with our largest long-range rocket, the A-9/A-10. However, we had not been able to start building the tunnel because it could not be called urgent.

Before I left Dr. Hermann I had to disappoint him once again.

I was forced to forbid work on the A-9 until further notice. Development of the A-4 had to be completed first. Only then could precious man hours be allotted to projects for the future.

As I was getting into my car to drive down the long concrete road to Test Stand VII I heard above my head the sound of a rocket motor. In the clear sky a small rocket-propelled aircraft, the Messerschmitt Me-163, was tearing almost vertically upward, leaving a brownish-white trail of smoke. Through my binoculars I watched this interceptor aircraft as, with its motor cut off and making a whistling sound, it described, like a tiny, tailless bird, great arcs and curves over Peenemünde. It swooped downward, looping the loop three or four times. Then the plane, losing height steadily, swept quietly in over the forest to land.

I remembered the work we had done on rocket motors for aircraft. We had begun as early as 1935. I recalled many different scenes and events.

At that time it was not for our own work that we were soliciting the interest of the Air Ministry. We were already aware of the importance of rocket propulsion for the development of fast aircraft. It had indisputable advantages, despite its high fuel consumption and short duration. It was potentially useful as a take-off aid for heavy bombers and as a power plant for very fast fighters climbing almost vertically, the so-called interceptors.

Our first power plant, the 650-pound motor, was already perfectly reliable when the firm of Junkers put a small aircraft, the "Junior," at our disposal. I still have a vivid recollection of the scene in the spring of 1936. After we had mounted the motor below the fuselage of the aircraft, which had been delivered without wings, von Braun himself ran the first test in the small arena of the big test stand at Kummersdorf. His face had grown pale but his eyes were sparkling. For the first time a liquid-propellant rocket motor had been attached to an airplane!

He was determined to try it out himself. The spherical tanks had been placed in the empty fuselage, and the operating levers and switches in the side wall near the pilot's seat.

At that time no one had thought of a use for it. As we wished to develop more powerful motors and build them into aircraft, we had to study the acceleration and behavior of the equipment when flying curves. For that purpose we built a large centrifuge, measuring about 50 feet. One end of the rotating steel frame carried the pilot's seat, braking equipment, and a newly developed, controllable power plant of 2200-pound thrust. The other end of the frame carried a counterweight. Von Braun did his dizzy laps. The motor worked perfectly and accelerations up to 5 g were measured. Von Braun got down happy, though somewhat dazed by his breathless merry-go-round.

Shortly afterward we installed this motor, provided with pressure tanks holding fuel for 90 seconds' duration, in a single-engined Heinkel He-112 as an auxiliary power plant. This was the first airplane with a rocket motor in its tail.

Test-stand experiments had progressed sufficiently by the end of 1936 so that flight tests could be undertaken. The purpose of the additional rocket power plant was to produce sudden bursts of speed in fighter aircraft at critical moments in dogfights—sometimes referred to as "superperformance."

In the spring of 1937 the first flight tests were carried out at the small airport of Neuhardenberg, northeast of Berlin. The pilot was Flight Captain Warsitz. He made two or three successful flights. In the next, Warsitz had just switched off the power again when to our dismay we saw him suddenly go into a crash dive and, without lowering the landing gear, set the plane in a splintering belly-flop in the scrub. We rushed up in a panic. Immediately after switching off he had noticed a smell of burning and, assuming the tail to be on fire, decided on an emergency landing. We found that the low back pressure created in the fuselage during flight had drawn the tongue of flame, which, without developing power, continued for a few seconds to issue from the nozzle after switching off, into the interior of the aircraft, and some cables had smoldered. The fairing between the exhaust nozzle and the inner walls of the airplane's tail had been inadequate. Unfortunately the machine had been so badly damaged in landing that we could make no further flights for the time being.

After we moved to Peenemünde, development work on behalf of the Air Force continued. At Test Stand IV we developed, under the direction of Engineer Dellmaier, assisted take-off devices for heavy bombers. Power plants of 2200-pound thrust each, lasting 30 seconds, were placed in two nacelles, jettisonable after exhaustion. They could be landed by parachute. Suspended starboard and port under the wings, they allowed the bomber to carry heavier loads or else permitted a shorter take-off run with normal load.

In 1939–40 a series of test flights took place in Peenemünde West with a Heinkel He-111 equipped with these auxiliaries. Only logistic difficulties, especially with reference to the liquid oxygen, finally caused the decision not to introduce this equipment into service, even though its performance was perfectly satisfactory. Assisted take-off units using hydrogen peroxide, made by the firm of Hellmuth Walter in Kiel, were eventually introduced in large numbers instead. The necessary tests had been carried out at Peenemünde West.

We had the same experience in developing a new controllable 2200-pound thrust power plant burning for 300 seconds, with pump propellant feed, for a rocket fighter intended to reach a height of 40,000 feet in 2 minutes. The Walter motor could be produced more quickly and was simpler in construction, but its performance was markedly inferior.

In the summer of 1938 the first rocket fighter, the He-176, took off in Peenemünde West. It looked somewhat uncertain and shaky as it tore round over the airfield in its first breathtaking curves.

The power plant developed by us was then installed in a new Heinkel He-112 for a burning time of 120 seconds and flown successfully several times. As bad luck would have it, the pilot lost control on one of the test flights, a considerable time after the rocket motor had been switched off, and the plane crashed.

When the war broke out we had to concentrate on the long-range rocket A-4, and were therefore compelled to abandon these projects.

The whistle of the Me-163 was still sounding in my ears when I got out of my car in front of the big assembly hall at Test Stand VII. Dr. Thiel and the test-stand engineer, Schwarz, were waiting for me. We passed through the little gate into the hall of brick and reinforced concrete nearly 100 feet high and 150 feet long.

As I talked to Dr. Thiel, listening with only half an ear to his familiar complaints about the virtually certain failure of our unit's system of forty-five different valves, all fully automatic, I watched a missile being mounted on one of the two large mobile test frames which occupied between them the whole of the right half of the wide hall. Since static tests had been going on daily for months, the crew had had so much practice that everything went like clockwork. Every movement counted. Without effort, the huge crane laid the rocket, its gymbal suspension ring already in place, into the open bearing bushes.

Dr. Thiel pointed to the long-range rockets standing vertically on their tail fins against the wall on the left, in three rows, one behind the other. Once again I was delighted by the perfect beauty of their shape. Dr. Thiel described in despairing tones how many bugs his test section had found in the motors, valves, or guidance components of the rockets delivered by the factory. The production of experimental missiles would have to be stopped until those we already possessed had been put in working order and fired. I let him go on talking. If he was not given any missiles to test he complained; if he was given any he still complained. It always did him good to let off steam. Like the rest of us, he was fascinated by his job. He would undoubtedly find some way of overcoming his difficulties. At my next visit he would be sure to have some new difficulty to complain of. In the end everything came off all right.

Two more missiles were standing on turntables in a corner at the end of the hall, framed in their wooden scaffolding with its various platforms and ladders. Countless cables and measurement pipes led through the wall of the hall to the testing laboratories of the department of electrical equipment, which had been

set up in an annex. We left the hall and passed the newly completed flow test stands. Here, after the missiles had been assembled,
flow tests were made under conditions simulating those occurring
at an actual firing. In the alcohol system we used alcohol, which
was recovered afterward; in the oxygen system we used water.
By means of these tests, recorded by flow-metering devices, we
established the figures for the propellant flow in each system and
excluded freak cases from our investigation. Our object was to
achieve an average performance figure by qualitative improvements and to speed up production and acceptance by reducing to a
minimum the tests provided for on individual components as delivered, and on the assembled missile.

We passed through the large gap in the surrounding wall that
protected test stand and launching site against high sea winds and
blown sand, and entered the wide arena. Facing us on rails stood
the powerful mobile test frame. It had been driven to a point
exactly above the center of the blast tunnel, which went down into
the ground and was furnished with an iron cooling-pipe system
at the impact point of the fiery exhaust. The concrete duct, nearly
25 feet wide, sloped gradually away to a depth of 20 feet, rising
again symmetrically on the other side.

The exhaust nozzle of the fully assembled rocket, vertically suspended in its gymbals and capable of turning in all directions,
was 25 feet above the upper edge of the cooling duct. An elevator
carried us to the various working platforms, where final preparations for the combustion trial were being made by experienced
craftsmen and engineers. The rocket had been fueled. We still had
about ten minutes to wait.

I went with Dr. Thiel to the observation and measuring bunker
built into the boundary wall at the narrow southern end of the
arena 150 yards away. All over the arena I could see the road
vehicles which had been brought in for tests standing ready for
the rocket. There was the big Meillerwagen with its erecting
boom, the small, slender Vidal for long hauls, and beside them
stood firing tables of the most diverse types, newly arrived cable
masts, and vehicles for special purposes.

I felt a heartening conviction that we would succeed. Only a month or two now and we should be over the worst.

I stood with Dr. Thiel behind the bulletproof glass door of the observation bunker and looked at the test stand, cleared of all crew members for the static test. The working platform had been drawn up. I now had a clear view of the black and white rocket, with its girdle of hoarfrost. The tiny white clouds of steam at the oxygen vent pipe drifted rapidly away before the light breeze blowing from the Peenemünde estuary.

Our missiles were fully automatic and we fired them out to sea. Any faulty valve, or relay that failed, any defect even in the smallest component of this complex machine, could throw the missile off its prescribed path, cause diminution of thrust, premature Brennschluss—or even an explosion.

The rockets, however, once they left the firing table, were always lost. We could never find out what had caused the failure. The guilty component nearly always ended up at the bottom of the blue-gray Baltic. I had therefore made a rule from the start that every rocket was to be tested with utmost care before it was passed for firing. All the separate components, as well as the entire unit, had to be checked and rechecked again and again. To ascertain reliability, performance, and control, a static burning of the complete missile had to take place on suitable test stands. The purpose of all this was to provide opportunity for anything which might occur in free flight to take place on the ground, where the behavior of the rocket could be studied. Consequently the building of test stands and testing gear ran like a red thread through the years of development. Only when we had got over our teething troubles would we be able to cut down on tests.

I had also ruled that all these ground tests, as well as preparations for actual firings, should be made in the open in whatever weather happened to prevail. I thought it a mistake to get the rockets ready in well-heated rooms, protected from the wind, to please the engineers, and bring them into the open only just before firing. After all, we did want to know how the rocket would behave at any temperature and under all sorts of wind conditions, to determine evaporation losses, to recognize in good time malfunctions due to atmospheric moisture, to develop heating apparatus for parts that might be disturbed in their function by the chill of the liquid oxygen, and above all to create suitable auxiliary equipment required for operational use at the front line.

The result of these measures was that when the rockets began to be used operationally, only 17 per cent of them failed to function, or developed control failure or other failures after take-off during the ascending portion of the trajectory. Later, when we had got into the swing, we actually reduced failures to 4 per cent, an astonishingly low figure with so complex and automatic a machine, especially when compared with nearly 28 per cent for the Fi-103 (V-1), a considerably simpler weapon in its entire structure.

The static firing went off without the slightest hitch. Flame formation appeared to be faultless. The missile obeyed without difficulty the commands transmitted by remote control to its control system. Swivel movements in all directions, turns about the longitudinal axis, and finally changes of direction, all went according to plan.

I next examined, in the measurement bunker, the inked diagrams of thrust and pressure at some fifteen measurement points in the interior of the rocket. Thrust on the stand, with a 1.0:0.85 mixture-ratio of oxygen to fuel, amounted to just over 25 tons. It would have been ideal if the form of our nozzle had been adjustable to varying outside pressure at varying heights. But this was not possible. We agreed therefore upon a mean value which would permit the expansion of gases to a pressure of 0.85 atmospheres at the exhaust nozzle exit. Nevertheless, when ambient pressure dropped during flight, thrust rose noticeably and finally reached the figure of 29 tons.

The diagrams showed a steady run and standard performance.

I went off with Schwarz through the long underground corridor that led from the measurement room beneath the wall of the arena to the stand. Along both sides of this corridor, taking up the entire wall space, ran double and triple rows of thick, heavy

measurement cables. We went down some steps and found ourselves in a big, very long room, beside the blast tunnel. Here the
cold-water pipes, nearly 4 feet in diameter and conveying 120
gallons per second, were connected with the molybdenum-steel
cooling-pipe system of the duct. The 3-foot concrete tunnel wall
radiated only a small amount of heat after the test.

We went up through a second, gradually rising corridor and
walked through the big pumphouse into the open air. Here were
the high wooden towers for recooling the water, and the water
tanks, nearly 25 feet high, built into the sand wall surrounding the
test arena.

I was separated now only by a last, low, pine-clad dune from
the broad sandy plain, covered with black cinder, of Test Stand
X. Its dark, even, cinder surface was interrupted here and there
by a patch of grass, a small, bright concrete apron, a wooden
platform or a small circle of loam stamped smooth. From here
test shots were fired to establish how various types of ground
would stand up in use. Everywhere Meillerwagens carrying rockets were standing, as well as rockets on firing tables. Special
service and tank cars were parked at regular intervals; flexible fuel
pipes led to connections in the rocket; cables were laid out and
assumed roads marked with white tape.

Here basic procedure for employment of the rocket in the field
was being worked out by practical experiment under the direction
of Engineer Klaus Riedel, to be incorporated later in field manuals.

My car was waiting for me. We drove past the high Test Stand I
and turned into the narrow concrete road laid right at the edge
of the woods and running from north to south past the long series
of other test stands.

I stopped for a short time at small Test Stand VIII to watch an
acceptance test. Here the 25-ton motors supplied by the factory
or by outside firms were subjected to a test run to determine performance. The bluish-red gas jet was projected through a wide,
double-walled, iron duct. Through a large number of small holes
in the inner wall of the duct huge quantities of water squirted
into the shining lance of the flame. During the 60 seconds of the

experiment enormous clouds of dense white steam rose from the mouth of the concrete blast tunnel, which was built to deflect the jet 90 degrees.

We were not satisfied with the design of our 25-ton motor. Ours was the first rocket motor with a thrust of 25 tons and a burning period of 1 minute, but the defect of the design was that it had been created on an extremely empirical basis. It was a hodgepodge of parts developed for different earlier motors, and too complex for easy manufacture. We were asking too much of the welders' craftsmanship. Even if the new welding equipment and automatic welding tools should prove adequate for the job, the number of man hours required to produce the motor was unreasonably high. To produce the fuel droplet mist, and to accomplish cooling by means of a film of alcohol, thousands of small injection holes and perforations had to be made in the burner cups and nozzle walls.

Dr. Thiel had already tried a simpler injection system, rows of ordinary holes in a flat headplate. But with large chambers this did not work so well.

Professor Beck of the Dresden College of Engineering had been working for about two years on the development of a circular slit injection nozzle. It was much easier to produce but so far we had succeeded in making it work properly only with small motors of less than 2000-pound thrust. With the 25-ton unit there were loud humming sounds of varying rhythms, a drop in performance, and serious vibrations of the chamber during test-bed running. We were therefore compelled, despite production difficulties, to continue for the time being with the eighteen-burner-cup chamber head.

Test Stand IX, nearing completion, lay farther south and was to be used for the Wasserfall—the large, remote-controlled anti-aircraft rocket, flying at supersonic speed. I drove round it and reached No. II, which served for test runs with a different fuel combination consisting of nitric acid and visol.[1] Then I came to No. IV, where we had tested power plants for installation in aircraft,

[1] "Visol" was the code name for vinyl isobutyl ether, which, with nitric acid, forms a hypergolic (self-igniting) combination.

and No. III, a small stand for horizontally mounted motors of up to 2200-pound thrust. Thence I went on to the pump and steam-turbine test stand. Here acceptance tests of our large propellant pumps and hydrogen-peroxide steam turbines took place. A refrigerating chamber which could be cooled by liquid oxygen enabled us to make tests at very low temperatures.

Finally I drove past No. VI, built as a replica of our large one at Kummersdorf and used until a year before for ground tests on the experimental rocket A-5. Hundreds of specimens had since been fired from the Greifswalder Oie, so No. VI was free for the Wasserfall, pending completion of No. IX.

From there I went to the great assembly workshop, part of the factory proper, and my goal, the Measurement House—the laboratory of the electrical department.

Dr. Steinhoff had been asking me for days to come and see him. For my own part, I had some research results I wanted to discuss with him. The problem was the reduction of the lateral dispersion of the A-4. It had been clear to us from the outset that this costly missile would not be worth while in war unless we could keep dispersion and especially lateral dispersion at a minimum. Hitherto we had had a total lateral dispersion at full range of about 11 miles. That was far too much. It was Dr. Steinhoff's task to devise means of reducing this to less than 1 mile. The wide dispersion was due to mistakes in adjustment, mounting tolerances in the guidance and control mechanisms, lack of stability of the gyroscopes even with minimum friction in the bearings, and a host of minor factors.

There was only one countermeasure we could take. We should have to make the rocket move in a guide beam during the burning period—that is, for the part of the trajectory during which it was powered and therefore steerable. Such radar beams had long been used for blind landing of aircraft, but we needed one that was much more sensitive. We could not use a beam which grew diffused with increasing distance from the transmitter. We wanted a vertical guiding "plane," of zero thickness, if possible a one-dimensional guiding "line." That would be the best. At the slightest deviation from this line the rocket would have to be steered back onto its course. To meet Allied interference, we would have to employ decimeter and later on centimeter waves, all this with a minimum of equipment both in the rocket and on the ground.

The leading firm in this field had been busy on the problem for years but had made no progress. It repeatedly promised delivery dates and then did not keep them. Whether these delays were due to our low priority, the firm's production burden of ordinary radar instruments, or the inadequate incentive of our small orders, I did not know, but my impression was that we were being systematically held up. Conference after conference brought no result. I could not account for this. What was useful to us must surely also be useful for other developments in the field of radar. At last I could see only one way out—to try to get development of our guide-beam devices incorporated into one of the most urgent of the state armament plans, the radar program. In the end I accomplished this. But I had overestimated Army influence on that program. Its head was also the man in charge of the development of our guide-beam apparatus. We simply did not get anywhere. Right up to the end of the war we had to struggle along with our original guide-beam device, an Air Force type which we had improved.

Even with this guide beam we met a succession of problems. We failed to reduce the 50-per-cent lateral dispersion of the A-4 to less than 1.5 miles. Results were, to be sure, considerably better than they had been without a guide beam but they did not by any means come up to what we might have achieved had our project been developed in time.

Exactly two years earlier, in June 1941, Steinhoff had asked me to accompany him on a test flight along a guide beam improved by his department. The Air Force had provided us with two planes for test-flying our equipment. In the spring of 1940 we had installed a fully automatic pilot, operated on a guide beam of 50 megacycles frequency; the 3-kilowatt transmitter was in the north of the island near the hook of Peenemünde. The central beam radiating from this transmitter pointed northeastward to the Danish island of Bornholm. Steinhoff was of the opinion that the plane, flying automatically the distance of 90 miles to Bornholm, would reach the same point on the island's shore every time with a deviation of only 20 yards if it were flown into the beam to within 1 degree of its direction 1½ miles from the transmitter. The total range of the transmitter was stated to be 125 miles.

Happy about this promising prospect, I took off with von Braun and Dr. Steinhoff for a beam-guided flight over the Baltic. As soon as the airplane had been aligned with the beam, Steinhoff left the pilot's seat and came to talk to us. The machine, fully automatic, flew along the beam on a straight course, very low over the water. Steinhoff mentioned a typical little red-roofed house on the beach as the point on the coast of Bornholm over which the aircraft would fly if it kept on the beam. After three-quarters of an hour we saw the coast of Bornholm rise up in the mists in front of us. Shortly afterward we flew over the little house. The survey party in Bornholm confirmed the precision of our arrival.

Today, after greeting Dr. Steinhoff in his office, I asked first about the latest research by Professor Vieweg of Darmstadt on the electrostatic charge on the rocket as it penetrated the earth's atmosphere. In his careful way, Dr. Steinhoff replied to my questions without committing himself to any definite figures. He wouldn't be pinned down to anything.

"Doctor Vieweg believes the electrostatic charge is less than twenty thousand volts."

"That seems very high to me. Wouldn't there be any visible discharge phenomena?"

"I don't think so, or we should have been bound to notice them at some time or other in measuring field strength from the telemetering equipment during flight. Doctor Vieweg believes that this charge has no effect on the electrical equipment of the rocket."

"Did the experiments on Test Stand Three throw any light?"

"The results tallied approximately with Doctor Vieweg's views. But there were various errors due to dust blowing around during the static test."

"Dust in the air and impurities in the gas jets do seem to have quite a big effect. The same thing happens in the case of ionization in the exhaust. At any rate I gather we don't have to worry about the electrostatic charge."

"One can't state that positively, but I think we probably don't."

"How much are our guidance signals affected by ionization in the exhaust?"

"Doctor Vieweg says he measured a maximum density of 10^6 ions to the cubic centimeter."

"That doesn't mean much to me. My question was, what effect does ionization have on our signals?"

"The field strength of the signals is considerably reduced. With our old fifty-megacycle sets we measured a decrease up to ninety per cent at Brennschluss distance. However, our signals have always come through all right up to now."

"And what happens with the five-hundred-megacycle set, that unfortunate motorized Würzburg giant, the 'rhinoceros'?"

"The decrease seems to be only ten per cent."

"But the rhinoceros is an impossible thing, Doctor. That monstrosity could never be used in active service. Have you been to see the Telefunken people lately? Are they making any progress with our centimeter guide beam?"

"I saw a lot of new things."

"My dear Doctor, I asked you whether they are making any progress."

"I believe—"

"I see! Well, I suppose I shall have to go and see them myself after all. What on earth will be the good of the A-4 if it's going to have a dispersion of eleven miles across the landscape? If the Telefunken people had put their shoulders to the wheel we should have been able to fire over a range of one hundred fifty miles, this year, with a total dispersion of less than one thousand yards. It's enough to make a man despair. But what was it you wanted to show me?"

"You must see our new simulators for testing the different control mechanisms and servomechanisms, and also the trajectory simulator which shows what an inadmissible increase there is in the oscillation amplitude of the rocket in the thin air, when the beam is switched on after forty-three seconds of flight near the end of the burning time."

"So you've already told me more than once. I'm beginning to get cold feet. What's Doctor Hermann's opinion? Isn't the aerodynamic damping adequate in rarefied air?"

"Because air density diminishes so fast toward the end of the powered flight, ram pressure falls rapidly too, and so does the natural aerodynamic oscillation figure. But the energy of the missile itself remains practically constant. Signals sent through the beam increase oscillation amplitude still further. Dispersion increases instead of diminishing."

"You don't quite convince me there, Doctor. You don't have to force the rocket suddenly off the straight course, nor do you have to use the beam only near Brennschluss time. If the rocket is taken right into the beam from the beginning and the slightest deviation corrected as it occurs, you shouldn't get much oscillation."

"I wouldn't care to swear to it. In any event I can prove that the effect exists."

"Well, all right, Doctor, show me what's new."

Most discussions with Steinhoff went on something like this. At first he had bubbled over with optimism and named the most fantastic figures and delivery dates. Then bitter experience had brought disappointment. He had grown cautious—too much so. But there was no doubt about his ability. His department was excellently managed and in the few years of its existence had done brilliant work, thanks to its outstandingly good staff.

We entered one of the many laboratories and saw a row of simulators of various designs, with control mechanisms mounted on them. A profusion of cables led to the adjoining electrical mixers, in which the different exterior and interior influences created during combustion time in the rocket were blended and transformed into a single signal transmitted to the servomechanism.

Here, too, the makers of our test simulators had been given the task of substituting simulators for time-consuming experiments carried out with the assembled missile on expensive test stands. The simulator was to be developed by various improvements until it was fully equal to its task. Factors to be investigated were the moment of inertia about the missile axis, the moments of aerodynamic forces, the air damping moment, and the moment of the vanes. In addition there were the characteristics of the guidance and control systems, the gains for "positional deviation" and its derivatives. By "positional deviation," we meant the angle of the axis of the missile to the position determined by the gryo, and the lateral offset from the guidance beam.

The total effect of all these factors, some of which were even time-changing variables, had been theoretically investigated with the help of stability calculations. The results now had to be checked in a practical laboratory experiment with the aim of reducing the extent of computing work and establishing the influence of each factor. Simulator technique had come into being.

During the first stage of development, the mechanical properties of the missile were represented by mechanisms such as weights and springs. The control equipment was real, the same that was slated for test firings. At the second stage, which Steinhoff showed me that day, the mechanical analogues were partly replaced by electrical ones. A programming device regulated the various factors just as they change in actual flight. The simulator was a convenient means of quickly testing their influence. The behavior of the missile in different flying conditions, and when certain signals, such as a guiding beam, were transmitted to it, was shown on measuring instruments and photographed on oscillograph tapes.

While Steinhoff and his engineers were explaining, I watched the work of the simulators which tested our control mechanisms. The usual vanes fastened to the hinge of the servomechanism were here replaced by long pointers moving over scales. I could see the sensitivity of the control equipment. A deflection, a swiveling movement of the table imperceptible to the naked eye, had scarcely begun before the pointers of the machine "opposed" it. The table with the "rocket" produced a few oscillations which soon faded, and then it resumed the direction given by the gyro.

I could follow accurately on the trajectory simulator the working of the control equipment during the whole burning time, and I saw the rocking of the oscillations about the course of flight when a guide-beam signal was given. I determined to have a chat with von Braun and Dr. Hermann about it.

It was nearly noon by the time I returned to the staff building, where the inevitable paper work awaited me.

After lunch I went with von Braun through the design office, stopping at board after board. Von Braun, as usual, had a lot of questions to ask and even more wishes he wanted fulfilled. We discussed the difficulties in the way of getting out blueprints for production and sought some way of overcoming them. Our tour led us, as though drawn by a magnet, to one particular place—the Preliminary Design Group, where, under Engineers Roth and Patt, our most cherished desires and hopes for the future must stand up to the first thorough test by calculation and take shape on great white sheets of paper.

Von Braun's imagination knew no bounds. He often regarded as an established fact something his perpetually laboring spirit wished to be true. He reveled in any project that promised to be on a gigantic scale, and, usually, in the distant future. I had to brake him back to hard facts and the everyday. I had to force him to go more deeply into things, to concentrate more, especially on questions of detail.

I knew that as soon as he really applied himself intensively to all the technical questions his indisputable genius would find the right answer. He had an almost incredible gift for retaining, out of a profusion of scientific data, literature, discussions, and visits to factories, the one important point that concerned our work; for seizing upon it, developing it in his mind, and putting it into action at the right spot. He forgot or dismissed everything else from his thoughts as useless lumber.

He was erratic at first and not completely persistent. He would go from one thing to another, but only until he had a clear idea of what he wanted to achieve. Then he would grow stubborn, and would not tolerate any impediments or deviations. With infinite shrewdness, and full steam ahead, he would pursue the course he considered to be the right one.

It was a never-ending joy to me to contribute to the development of this great rocket expert by training him from his youth during the years of our work together. I had the great advantage of knowing him intimately, both his strong points and his obvious weak ones, the way he worked and even his intentions. Impelled as I was by the firm resolve to help, there was no limit to what I could do to smooth the way to our common goal. No quarrel or unbridgeable difference of opinion ever darkened our relationship. We appreciated and helped each other.

Here in the Preliminary Design Group, von Braun could really let himself go, for this was where our plans for the future were born.

Our aim from the beginning was to reach infinite space, and for this we needed speeds hitherto undreamed of. Range and velocity were the great landmarks that guided our thoughts and actions.

The objective was clear. Our first task was to create the premises necessary for success. The A-4 was only an intermediate stage. Like all goals once reached by creative toil, it ceased to claim our whole interest from the moment of fulfillment. We wanted to do more. War conditions, however, restricted us to small-scale operations.

It was easy enough to see that one-step rockets, which had to go on carrying the useless deadweight of the empty tanks and heavy motors all the way, could never have their range appreciably increased. If we were going to add to the rocket's deadweight, already reduced to a minimum, any considerable payload for long distances, even a change of propellants would be of very little use to us. The only exception would be a combination of hydrogen and oxygen with a theoretical exhaust velocity of over 10,000 feet per second. But this was for the time being out of the question because of the difficulty of handling liquid hydrogen. Nor would

a bigger rocket help much. Years of research on the widest varia-
tions in propellants at universities and technical colleges and at
our works had proved that all those which could be used and—
an essential point—were actually available, differed in performance only by about 20 per cent. That was no good to us. We
meant to bridge much longer distances.

With an improved, lighter A-4 type of one-step rocket with relatively bigger tanks we might be able to achieve a range of 250
to 300 miles—but mainly at the expense of the payload, that is,
the warhead.

We had to break new ground. Why need the rocket strike the
ground at a speed of nearly 2000 miles per hour? If we gave it
wings and took advantage of their lift, changing the trajectory
into a glide after a suitable time interval, we could use the energy
hitherto expended in making big holes in the ground to increase
range.

Calculations showed that with such a structure we might achieve
a range of 342 miles, which would be double that of the A-4. Our
rocket, however, would then become a supersonic airplane with
fully automatic guidance. Its course would be through the earth's
atmosphere and through almost airless space.

This was 1943. No airplane had yet flown at supersonic speed.
Since the spring of 1940 our wind tunnel had been used successfully for development of suitable wings and other basic research
for the designers.

Thus the A-9 came into being.

Hundreds of calculations were made to plot the trajectory that
would give the greatest range. Finally the missile was planned to
reach, at a height of about 12 miles, a maximum speed of 2800
miles per hour, and then go into a shallow curving glide with a
peak of nearly 18 miles. On arrival over the target, at a height
of about 3 miles, it was planned to dive vertically, like the Fi-103
(V-1).

It was only a step from the pilotless A-9, with fully automatic
guidance, to the piloted A-9. This extremely fast aircraft, with a
wing area of only about 145 square feet, had no military sig-

nificance. Special gear enabled it to land, after traveling about 400 miles in 17 minutes, at a speed of only 100 miles per hour.

This development of the A-9, however, did not satisfy our ambitions. We wanted to cover thousands of miles. Our own private and exclusive sphere of activity began only beyond the extreme limit of the range of the heaviest aircraft.

Only by abandoning the one-step for the multi-step rocket—that is, by dropping the deadweight when it has served its purpose, thereby improving the mass-ratio of the rocket, could we hope for an almost incredible increase in range.

This was the origin of the A-9/A-10 project. The object here was to cause the motor of the second step (the A-9) to begin firing only when the missile had reached a high speed by means of its first step, which acted as a booster.

Catapulting was an alternative method of imparting a high starting speed to the A-9. On the basis of calculations and experience on V-1 launching sites, a long, inclined catapult had been designed, capable of giving the A-9 a launching speed of 800 miles per hour. This would have been sufficient for the fully fueled rocket to fly on smoothly, after leaving its launching ramp.

A better plan, however, and one which greatly improved range, was to construct the A-10, weighing 87 tons and with a total propellant capacity of 62 tons, as the first step of the combined A-9/A-10. The A-9 was placed on top of the A-10. The latter had a thrust of 200 tons for 50 to 60 seconds and gave the rocket a speed of 2700 miles per hour. After exhaustion of the first step the A-9 would be ignited and lift out of the A-10. The A-9 was to tilt fairly sharply soon after and reach a peak altitude of 35 miles. Then the long supersonic glide was to begin. Meanwhile the A-10, equipped with brake flaps and parachute, was to descend into the sea for recovery and later re-use.

The A-9, beginning to operate at a great height, would acquire an additional velocity of 3600 miles per hour, resulting in a maximal velocity of about 6300 miles per hour, at the moment its motor cut off. As a result of this high velocity it would cover 2500 miles in about 35 minutes. Like the single-step A-4, this two-step rocket was to take off vertically and obviate the need for elaborate launching installations.

Countless trajectories were calculated by our outstanding expert in flight mechanics and ballistics, Dr. Steuding, and all the factors involved, such as the earth's curvature and rotation, were taken into consideration. Guidance systems were investigated and development of the missile began.

In the summer of 1943, work on this project, which had fully occupied large sections of our establishment, had ceased for several months. I had forbidden all further work on the plan in our engineering branches, because of the urgency of the A-4. Only the Preliminary Design Group was permitted to carry on.

During our frequent visits to this department we had repeatedly and thoroughly discussed these plans, due for practical development at an early date, as well as the optimal trajectory of the two-step rocket. We had foreseen and planned for its use in time of peace. Very fast stratospheric rocket aircraft, traveling at high supersonic speed, had reached design stage. They would be able to cross from Europe to America in 40 minutes.

Once we reached this stage the horses fairly bolted with us. With our big rocket motors and step rockets we could build space ships which would circle the earth like moons at a height of 300 miles and at a speed of 18,000 miles per hour. Space stations and glass spheres containing the embalmed bodies of pioneers of rocket development and space travel could be put into permanent orbits around the earth. An expedition to the moon was a popular topic too.

Then we dreamed of atomic energy, which would at last give us the necessary drive for flight into the infinity of space, to the very stars.

It was now four in the afternoon. I had gone up on the lofty concrete platform of Test Stand I. Facing me, in the arena of Test Stand VII, 250 yards away, the first sparks of the pyrotechnic igniter were just falling from the exhaust nozzle of an experimental rocket about to be fired.

We always launched our A-4's from Peenemünde out to sea. It was only with the small rockets, A-3 and A-5, that we went over to the Oie to fire. We were taking a big risk and we knew it. We needed luck and we had it. Control often failed on the rockets and they went hopelessly off course. We had installed a device which enabled us to cause Brennschluss at will by radio. The fire-control officer, stationed on the high roof of the assembly workshop, had to time the signal so that the rocket crashed harmlessly in the woods, on the vast expanse of the airfield or in the Peenemünde estuary, before it reached the mainland with its villages and towns. So far all had gone well.

In the afternoon sunlight, shining from a sky of cloudless blue, I could see clearly far across the gentle swell of the gray Baltic every feature of the Greifswalder Oie, the lighthouse, the woods, the houses, and the cliffs. Tomorrow there would be rain. When visibility was so good, it always meant a change in the weather.

I watched, through my binoculars, the multitude of ducks in the green, reedy foreland of the bay, followed the flight of the white-tailed eagles, and enjoyed the colorful splendor of the early summer afternoon.

I had time for it. Once more the "Peenemünde minute" had lasted about 11 minutes. It looked at though something had gone wrong. The engineers in the observation bunker facing me had delayed switching on for the start. But at last all was ready. The preliminary stage of low thrust began working. For 3 or 4 seconds the fiery jet sent the dry dust of the concrete platform flying in all directions. Then the main stage started. The cables were cast off. The rocket took off.

But it did so slowly, very slowly. The heavy missile, weighing 12.5 tons, with its good-luck symbol painted between two fins, rose only 15 feet above the firing table. Then it stood still! It stood upright in the air, showing no desire to turn over or to revolve about its longitudinal axis.

It was an unbelievable sight. At any moment the rocket would topple or fall back, crash and explode. I involuntarily stepped aside to get at least some cover behind one of the thick iron pillars of the test stand. But I still kept my binoculars on the rocket. It hung at the same height above the firing table.

There must have been an interruption in the output of the steam generator for the propellant-pump turbine. The pump was not working at full power. It was feeding only enough propellants to the chamber to enable the thrust to counterbalance the weight of the rocket.

The film operator, Kühn, had taken up his position facing me, on the wall of the test stand. He must have had good nerves. The rocket hung in the air just 100 yards away. Nothing daunted, he calmly focused his camera on it. He certainly knew from experience that the moment the projectile fell back he would be in mortal danger. He just went on cranking. There was no point in calling to him. The tremendous roar of the motor drowned every other sound.

Our exhaust vanes were doing a wonderful job. The rocket stood unsupported in the air, as straight as a ramrod.

Only 4 seconds had passed, 4 seconds that seemed unbelievably long. The rocket was bound to topple now. The tilt would now begin automatically. The rocket must fall.

The thrust remained constant. The rocket grew lighter owing to the steady fuel consumption. Almost imperceptibly, yard by yard, it began to climb. Its nose turned very gradually eastward. Now the projectile began to travel. At a height of 30 to 40 feet it moved slowly, still practically upright, toward the cameraman. He went on cranking.

I caught my breath. Just a little more tilt and the rocket would certainly capsize and explode in the wide area of the test stand or on the wall.

It rose only slightly as it steadily approached the daring operator behind the camera. It was now 60 to 70 feet up and hung in the air at a considerable angle.

Now it was over the wall. Kühn knelt down and pointed his camera almost straight upward. It was going to be some film!

In my excitement I left the cover of my iron pillar. I wanted to dash across and drag the man from the open. Any moment now the crash would come.

I no longer cared about the rocket. I knew what was bound to come. I had eyes only for the man. I saw him get up slowly, still cranking. His camera was now practically horizontal. Then he pointed it diagonally down from the high wall. Boom!

But this was impossible! I could have screamed aloud! Smoke, flames, fragments of sheet-metal, branches, and sand whirled through the air. The rocket had crashed into the sandhills 40 yards beyond the wall and exploded.

The cameraman was still cranking. Taking a deep breath, I lowered my binoculars. My heart was beating painfully fast. Then I was filled with an immense pride. Only in this fashion, only with men like this, could we finish the job that lay before us.

CHAPTER 14

BLACK DAY

On the afternoon of Tuesday, August 17, 1943, I had assembled at the long table in my Peenemünde office Colonel Stegmaier; the chief of the Pre-Production Works, Ministerial Councilor Schubert with his works manager, Chief Engineer Rudolph; the chairman of Production Planning, Engineer Stahlknecht; directors von Braun, Steinhoff, and Thiel; and Rees, director of the experimental workshop.

Behind the gaily printed curtains, with their stylized red griffins and North German cathedrals, the big windows stood wide open toward the west. The subdued light emphasized the clear outlines and pleasing colors of the room, adorned with handsome, gleaming furniture, quantities of flowers, rugs and pictures.

The padded doors leading to the next room were closed. Telephone calls were being taken by my adjutant. We were in private conference.

For days the sun had been blazing down on the arid, sandy soil of the island of Usedom. We were longing for a cooling thunderstorm. In this oppressive atmosphere an excited discussion had been going on for some hours. The collision of opinions was hard and unsparing. The *casus belli* was the steadily increasing incompatibility between the development and production departments.

Engineer Stahlknecht again complained bitterly about the development section and the delays in turning out production blueprints, pointing out the consequences to our A-4 schedule. Von Braun, Thiel, and Rees disclaimed responsibility, blaming the lack of trained employees in the administrative offices

147

of the planning, design, and pre-production departments. Stahl-knecht concluded by saying, "I must state once more, and in this matter we are presumably all of one mind, that the Degen-kolb schedule, with its output of nine hundred units a month from January 1944, cannot be carried out. Nor can the reduced schedule which I drew up get going soon unless I get blueprints from development by October first. The biggest bottleneck is pre-production designs, which come in so very late and are no sooner delivered than they are fundamentally changed again, so that it's impossible to—"

Professor von Braun jumped up excitedly to interrupt him. "If we're to start criticizing each other, I want to send the criticism home where it belongs. I need not tell you, General, that the special A-4 production committee under Degenkolb created in January has not lightened our labors. On the contrary, it has held up our real job, which is development. We didn't get the personnel we needed and asked for so urgently. The few skilled men arriving now after months of delay are untrained and there-fore give us no sort of relief. The production and redesign offices are already working at breakneck speed, with a staff inadequate in every respect. The work we still have to do is so enormous that we shall never make the deadline of October first. How can we have production tools designed and produced when we're not clear ourselves about the final form of the finished article? Raw material difficulties keep on forcing us to make designs with fresh materials said to be in better supply. I can only say that I am desperately sorry your agreement was ever given to the Degen-kolb schedule. I ask you most earnestly to report to higher au-thority that the A-4 project is for the time being impossible to execute. We've first of all got to develop in peace and quiet a prototype we can mass-produce and then go on to blueprints for production.

"Furthermore, I don't believe Degenkolb is the right man to manage our production schedule. He may be good at locomotives but he knows nothing whatever about our complicated machine or the ground installations it needs. How can our difficult production problems be entrusted to a man who has only one answer to all requests: 'Your difficulties don't interest me. You've got to help yourselves.' Or else he bawls, 'Get that output or you lose your job!' I can see disaster ahead."

Von Braun had spoken with steadily mounting excitement. Regaining his calm with an effort, he sat down.

Dr. Thiel spoke next. "I must refuse to confirm the rocket motor as ready for production. Industry won't execute small orders for separate components needed for the experimental and pre-production output. It wants the mass order right away. The components it does turn in aren't in any way up to standard. The motor is too complicated and very far from suitable yet for mass production."

Rees at once hastened to back him up. "Yes, we get a whole lot of rejects among the components. The result is that the output of experimental units comes to a full stop. On top of that the launching people keep on wanting just another quick alteration. Nearly eighty per cent of the rockets passed to the test field and accepted come back with requests for modification and clutter up production. It's been nearly ninety per cent behind schedule for the last few months. Now I hardly know myself what the standard unit ought to look like. I agree that the Degenkolb schedule is impracticable and also ask for a postponement."

I was facing a united front. Were these my first enthusiastic associates, whom nothing could dismay? Were they already losing their nerve over this job? What had happened to the conquerors of space?

To my own surprise I kept inwardly calm; I would manage them all right. The difficulties which seemed insurmountable to them were really nothing more than the inevitable preliminary problem of starting mass production of so novel an invention. I was determined to speak my mind.

"Gentlemen, the difficulties you believe you cannot cope with are known to me also. I did not support the Degenkolb schedule, but for the sake of peace and quiet I forbade you to fight it. Nowadays one has to make big demands to get a little. Degenkolb has done an amazing amount for us with no special authority or priority.

"But now—for the last six weeks, to be exact—grading to top priority has at last given us the firm basis we need for the schedule. Do give the resulting measures a chance to mature! I fear we may get too much help for our comfort. For instance, we got the antiaircraft protection we asked for within twenty-four hours. We've been allotted all the raw materials we asked for. Personnel is streaming in. In the last fortnight over twelve hundred men have arrived.

"I must ask you to check again whether, in accordance with my order at the end of last year, all development work on long-term projects of any kind has ceased.

"You really must stop saying we are not ready yet and can't set terms of delivery for subassemblies and components. We have lost at least six months for this reason alone. My own view is that we long since reached a stage of development that justifies our starting a large experimental and pre-production manufacturing program.

"In this war inventions have actually been put into mass production at a far lower stage of development. Manufacture of the Tiger heavy tank got its start from pencil drawings. You must really stop trying to introduce one improvement after another.

"The snag up here is that we have too many brains and ideas jostling each other in one spot. From now on I forbid any alteration in the rocket designs which is not absolutely essential. Any suggested improvements can be tested, if we have the time and material, and then consolidated and incorporated at some later stage in the mass product.

"I will give my agreement to the placing of full-scale orders on the basis of the present stage of development, even at the risk of modifications later or of unserviceability. We have got to get on with the job.

"Gentlemen, I consider you all very fine development engineers, but unfortunately you are not experienced production men. What is giving you such a headache now is only the familiar teething

troubles of any mass-production project. I have told you that before, and often enough. Have any of you anything more to say?"

Dr. Thiel indicated that he had. He had been sitting with his
lips spasmodically contracting and his head bent, playing nerv-
ously with his pencil. He had seemed not to be listening. As he
directed his oddly gleaming eyes, behind the flashing lenses of
his spectacles, upon me, I read determination and profound grief
in the ghastly pallor of his features.

"General," he began, "I am in despair. For months now we have
had one breakdown after another. We expected too much of our
A-4. In present conditions the job just can't be done. Our machine
is a flying, fully automatic laboratory. To put it into mass production is sheer madness. We aren't through with development
by a long way. I consider it out of the question that any Army
firing crew, even after years of training, will be able to carry out
the necessary operations under battle conditions. They are beyond the capacity of any soldier.

"If you persist in your point of view I must decline all further
work. I see no possibility that we shall achieve our aim before
the war is over. The project must be abandoned. I have given
the whole matter thorough consideration and ask to be allowed
to resign. I intend to join a technical college as lecturer in thermo-
dynamics."

That was our first thunderbolt. The ground began to tremble
beneath our feet. Dr. Thiel, the moving spirit of the revolt, was
instantly joined by Rees, the managing director, and, after some
hesitation, even by von Braun. The most critical hour of all our
work together had struck.

Dr. Thiel's nerves had given way through overwork. In the past
few months he had sent me several notes in the same vein. I did
not accept the resignation. I remained inflexible. I demanded
tireless continuance of the work. As for any anxiety about the
ability of the troops to handle the weapon, I said that could be
left to me. Once again I explained the terms of reference within
which we must strictly confine our work.

"You, gentlemen, your test field engineers and technicians, are charged with the duty of testing and making fit for launching every single experimental rocket that comes into the test field, despite all changes in interior equipment.

"The task of the troops is different. According to plan they'll receive thirty rockets a day of a single type. The individual soldier knows his own part but is not concerned with the whole picture. He has *one* job to do—take a certain reading, or pull a certain switch. If for any reason he can't do it he will apply to the battery engineer, who knows all about the rocket and can decide whether it can be passed for launching or must be replaced. It will be Colonel Stegmaier's duty, in conjunction with the test-field staff, to draw up a manual on the handling and preparation of the missile for launching.

"It will be your duty, gentlemen, to stick to the standard type as it is now, and fire, fire, and fire experimental series until you have it fit for production and use in the field. I am convinced that the troops, once their enthusiasm is aroused, will cope famously with the weapon in a surprisingly short time."

While I was still talking I noticed that my colleagues were slowly calming down. Cool reflection was superseding their gloom.

Professor von Braun was the first to come round. He made useful suggestions. I breathed again. I had managed at a critical moment to rescue our project and our common labors. The odd thing was that I felt no release from tension now that the danger was past. I was restless and filled with vague forebodings.

After the meeting ended, I decided to make a tour of the works. I felt I needed distraction from my thoughts. In spite of its outcome, I had been much shaken by the dispute that afternoon. I needed to renew my confidence and energy by seeing the work in progress.

Outside, the motionless air was still sultry and oppressive. Deep in thought, I went to my car and drove to the big assembly hall of the Experimental Series Works, the building of which had been held up for a whole year because of low priority. It was now almost ready and planned to go into mass production to cover a third of the Degenkolb schedule. I passed through a small door in the roughly boarded 60-foot-high main entrance into the hall, which rose to a height of 100 feet. The white roughcast walls gave the room, with its five divisions, its central aisle 200 feet wide, and its four side aisles seperated by pillars, an almost solemn appearance at this evening hour. I crossed the double railroad track leading into the hall and went up the ramp to the assembly hall proper, 80 feet high.

From there the view of the depth of the central aisle, over 600 feet long, hemmed in on each side by sixteen strong, square, gleaming concrete pillars, foreshortened from this point, and the rear wall fading into blue mists, once again held me spellbound. I lingered a long time. Potent joy swept over me. I wanted to see this hall thronging with happy, contented workers. I must hear in it the roaring, pounding, whistling, humming, ringing, infinitely varied sounds of work actually going on. I was more than ever certain that we would pull it off!

Outside, twilight had fallen. I drove slowly through the evening peace of the woods to the mess.

CHAPTER 15

FLAMING NIGHT

After dinner I sat at the low, circular, glass-topped table in the paneled Hearth Room, lit by the festive glitter of brass chandeliers, conversing with Professor von Braun, Dr. Steinhoff, and our guest of the evening, Hanna Reitsch, the test pilot. Curled up in a deep armchair, this elegant, energetic, clear-headed, and courageous woman told us about her life, work, and ambitions. The short coat of her dark-blue costume was adorned with the Iron Cross, First Class, and the brilliants of the pilot's badge. She shared with Professor von Braun recollections of gliding experiences over the Kurische Nehrung in East Prussia. Whenever anything brought her to Peenemünde we were always glad to see her.

Listening to the laughter of these young people, who cheerfully took all the surprises of technology in their stride, with their eyes on the future, I felt less oppressed by the serious worries of the afternoon. Neither von Braun nor Steinhoff showed any signs of pessimism or despair. They had already started making plans again and were full of the heartiest optimism. Toward half-past eleven, tired out with the heat and the care and excitement of the day, I was walking the few steps that led to one of the guest houses when the air-raid sirens howled the "early alarm."

It was not a new experience for us. The British airmen usually gathered over the central Baltic before they flew south with their load of bombs for Berlin. Hitherto we had played 'possum. Our antiaircraft defense had orders to fire only if we were actually being raided. All was quiet. The black-out was flawless; it was constantly checked.

Suddenly I noticed that from one angle the camouflage of the tile roofs was showing up and that the deep shadows of the houses were making sharp black patterns on the gleaming silver of the lawns and roads. The full moon!

Worry gripped me again. From my room I called up air-defense headquarters.

"Allied formations massing over the central Baltic, north of Rügen. Direction of approach not yet known."

I got into bed and soon fell into a quiet, dreamless slumber. I could not have been asleep long before I woke with a start.

S-s-s-st—bang!

So Stölzel was doing his experimental firing after all.

S-s-s-st—bang! S-s-s-st—bang!

The windowpanes rattled. Yet I had told Stölzel to set the time fuzes so as not to disturb the peaceful slumbers of Peenemünde.

S-s-s-st—bang! S-s-s-st—bang! S-s-s-st—bang!

Well! And I had given him permission to fire only five of the fifteen rounds available. And why this rapid fire! What possible chance was there of getting decent measurements? He would catch it from me in the morning! Half-asleep, I went on counting.

S-s-s-st—bang!

Nineteen, twenty, twenty-one—what? Twenty-one? Something wrong there. That couldn't be Captain Stölzel, who had asked my permission that evening to carry out test firing during the night with his anti-dive-bomber tank. It was not the 110-pound explosive charge of the 11-inch powder rocket which had awakened me from my first deep slumber and set the windows of my room rattling.

At once I was wide awake. Yes, those were the antiaircraft guns, the roaring, sharp double reports of the heavy batteries stationed at Lake Kölpin and along the edge of the airfield, mingled with the muffled detonations of the batteries on the opposite bank of the Peene and at Karlshagen. At intervals the light 20-millimeter guns barked from their elevated positions above the woods and from the roofs of the highest buildings. The 37-millimeter gun from the Gaaz harbor outpost was sending up many-colored strings of pearls, with a "plop, plop, plop," into the sky.

Peenemünde was under air attack!

I switched on my bedside lamp and reached for the telephone. The command shelter was busy. It would be! I jumped out of bed and had breeches and socks on in record time. Where the hell were my riding boots? Of all the nights the steward must have have chosen this one, late as it had been, to take them out of the anteroom to clean. I had to make do with slippers.

S-s-s-st—crash! S-s-s-st—crash! S-s-s-st—crash!

Then another three!

The first windowpanes tinkled out. Tiles came hurtling and clashing down the sloping roof, smashing on the ground. Not much time to lose. Well, for the moment, tunic over pajama coat would do. Now for overcoat, cap, gloves, and cigarcase. Out with the light and—BANG!

Some blast! That must have been a land mine not very far away. This time every windowpane blew out and the rest of the tiles came down. The frame of the hall door had been driven outward and was jammed. I managed to push through it. The glass door of the vestibule had been torn from its hinges and was lying on top the splinters of its lately leaded green glass. I found it was not exactly easy to walk over broken glass in soft slippers. The heavy oaken outer door had been blown out and lay on the steps leading down to the garden path.

I stood transfixed. The scene that met my gaze had a sinister and appalling beauty of its own.

I was confronted, as though through a rose curtain of gauze, by an almost incredible stage setting in subdued lighting and colors. Artificial clouds of mist rolled past me. Enormous fires must be raging somewhere. The moon shone through these fragile, cottony clouds, lighting up the planted pine forest, the roads, and the bushes. Everything was covered with white sand like sifted sugar. The buildings of the administrative wing, so far as I could distinguish them through the veiling mists, the drafting rooms, the development works, and the canteen appeared and disappeared at intervals through the rose-red fog like menacing shadows. Overhead was the star-strewn night sky with the beams of the searchlights whisking to and fro.

While one's startled eyes took in this scene, with its ever-changing colors, one's ears were assaulted by the continual barking and cracking of the AA guns, the reports of the bursting shells, the thunderous impact of the bombs, and the monotonous drone of the four-engined bombers.

I saw figures in front of the concrete shelter only a few yards away and recognized von Braun and Ministerial Councilor Schubert.

"I suppose you forgot all about me!" I called to them.

"No, we were just coming to get you."

"What the devil's it all about?" I asked. "Ten to one the AA were too keen and brought this down on us."

"No, no! This time they're really going for us."

"What reports have come in?"

"The lines to the Pre-Production Works, the settlement, and Karlshagen camp are out. The last message from the settlement warden said seven bombs had come down there."

"That certainly sounds grim."

Suddenly we heard a rushing and hissing sound, growing louder and louder, right overhead.

We dashed like lightning through the door of the shelter. Inside, a crowd of abruptly awakened and hurriedly dressed people huddled in the long, brightly lit room. Here one could hear only faintly the "plop, plop, plop" of the sticks of bombs bursting in the muffling sand. The AA fire sounded incredibly far away. Now and then the bunker shuddered and reeled like a ship in a storm. Faces grew paler and eyes bigger with unspoken questions.

I rang the command post and had the chief warden on duty summoned to the telephone.

"Report, please."

"Soon after midnight the first wave flew south over Peenemünde without dropping any bombs, headed for Berlin. The AA transmitter gave that as the probable target. About twelve-fifteen, wave after wave arrived over Peenemünde, coming from Rügen. The first few bombs fell into the Peene in front of the harbor. No damage reported to test stands so far. As far as I've been able to see, the Measurement House is on fire, the assembly workshop blazing, and the component and repair shops starting to burn. I haven't managed to get farther south yet. The lines to the Pre-Production Works and the settlement went dead directly after the first report of the seven bombs. The power station on the Peene is supposed to have been bombed too. That line's out as well. The works fire brigade was here a few minutes ago and I put them to work on the components shop. I've sent an urgent request to Karlshagen for reinforcements. With some of the wardens I've just been moving the big cable-drums, which were on fire, away from the back wall of the workshop. It looks as though we have saved the hall. The scrap dump behind the tool and fixture shop is burning."

"All-out raid on Peenemünde, then! Send runners to the Pre-Production Works, the settlement, and Karlshagen camp. I want to know what's happened there and when we can expect the Labor Service and the Northern Experimental Command companies. I'm coming over to you at once."

I looked at the time. It was thirty-five minutes past twelve.

Just as I was leaving the shelter someone handed me my riding boots, which he had fetched from the steward's room. I pulled them on and left the shelter with von Braun.

The scene had changed. Great fires were painting dark red the ubiquitous fog, now thickened with stinging smoke. Bright flames were darting from many places on the roof of the construction bureau. Glowing sparks whirled upward in dense clouds of smoke. The attic windows shone red. Some rafters on the rest-house roof were on fire. The mess and canteen were still dark. All round us, on the roads and in the grounds, the hissing thermite incendiaries shone dazzlingly white. Among them burned the sprays of the phosphorus canisters. It was a weird sight indeed.

"Von Braun, you will take over the construction bureau with all the men in the shelter and the Air Force construction labor gang. Try to restrict the fire to the top floor. Get a hose from the fire brigade. Schütz, who's in charge of the brigade, can help you. If you can't check the fire, try to get the safes, cabinets, records, and drawings out. This holds whether the raid goes on or not.

"Councilor, you can deal with the guest house. If you can't save the place, clear it! I'm going to the works. I want to know what's happened there, and where I can best use the help I hope Karlshagen will send soon."

A ten-year-old boy ran up to me. He said, "Sir, father told me to report to you that a land mine's come down by the telephone exchange. The side wall's fallen in. Incendiaries have set the roof on fire. He wants two or three men to help him. Then he thinks he can save the exchange."

I detailed two men to go with the boy and hurried across the forecourt of the construction bureau and through the portico to the area inside the gate. The old office barracks, which still housed the paymaster's office, the print and binding shops, and a few minor offices, was enveloped in flames and past all hope of saving. Retiring before the heat, I skirted a big bomb crater and made my way along the north side of the construction bureau to the main avenue of the development works.

Out of the fog loomed two men who were vainly attempting to salvage more material from the burning barracks of the apprentices' workshop. I could see a small fire beginning on the roof of the boiler house. If we were not to freeze the following winter the place would have to be saved. I sent the men up to the roof.

I hurried along the main avenue to the command shelter. The buildings to my right and left seemed all right. As far as I could tell for the moment, it was the eastern part of the area that had suffered most.

The chief warden on duty reported to me. The tool and fixture shop had been saved. I dashed off with two wardens to the Measurement House.

Flights of bombers were passing uninterruptedly over the area. There was a distant, hollow rumble of many bombs falling, mingled with the noise of AA guns. All one's senses were concentrated on the whistle of bombs dropping close. Alternately throwing ourselves down and leaping up, we reached the west side of the Measurement House containing the Flight Instruments, Guidance, and Measurement Department, at the time the most valuable part of the works. The windows were dark. Behind the building a big fire seemed to be raging. I rushed round the corner and beheld the assembly workshop on fire in several places. The big entrance gates, 60 feet high, were burning. Tongues of flame shot, crackling and hissing, out of the shattered windows of the extension buildings. Iron girders, twisted and red hot, rose above the outer walls. Parts of the roof structure collapsed, crashing down into the interior. Help would be too late here. In the midst of misfortune I felt momentarily glad that some months before we had transferred the assembly of experimental rockets to the repair workshop of the Pre-Production Works.

Already the three barracks east of the Measurement House were practically burned down. A tremendous wall of heat stopped us in our tracks.

I looked at the windows in the east façade of the Measurement House. Many of them shone brightly. Good heavens! The heat of the burning barracks had set fire to the wooden sashes! I took my two men along and we divided the floors between us. A fire extinguisher hung in front of almost every door. In 15 minutes we had saved the Measurement House, which was indispensable to the continuance of our work.

I left the men as a fire watch and ran to the component workshop. There I found the fire brigade at work. Jets of water pumped from reservoirs were playing on the burning storehouses and office buildings, alight with brilliant flames of every hue. Great masses of steam mingled with the dark smoke to form dense gray clouds. There wasn't much I could do here. I would have to wait for reinforcements to prevent the fire's spreading from the stockrooms to the workshop itself.

The lumber storage yard behind the component workshop was blazing uncontrollably. The scrap shed, which had been recon-

structed as a storage building, was also in flames, as was the materials reception depot. The entire length of the garage was on fire.
From the gasoline station brilliant flames were leaping sky high.

Turning, I saw a bright light in one of the windows of the Diesel
locomotive depot and accumulator charging station. I opened the
door with my master key, seized the fire extinguisher, here as elsewhere ready for use, and in a few seconds had put out the blazing
piles of packing cases and discards.

I dashed back again to the construction bureau. I arrived sweat-
ing with the heat of the fires and blackened with soot and ashes.

The forecourt was filling up with safes, furniture, and files. The
fires in the west and north sections seemed to have been put out.
In the east section the flames had spread to the second floor. The
fire brigade was in action at that point.

I turned to look at the guest house. It was only three-quarters
of an hour since I had run across to the command shelter. The
house looked done for. The whole top floor was in flames.

What on earth was holding up the fire brigade and the reinforcements from the Pre-Production Works, the camp, and the
settlement? What had happened to the Labor Service, which, according to the emergency plan, should have arrived at once in
trucks?

While I was instructing Schütz to send out another runner, Frau
Zanssen with her three children appeared at the entrance to the
shelter. Her house had been severely damaged by blast. The two
girls were rather subdued and quickly vanished into the shelter.
Five-year-old Gerhard planted himself in front of me, his hands
in his pockets, laughing all over his face. "I say, Uncle Sepi, what
a lovely fire!"

Angelic innocence! I chased him under cover. Steinhoff, too,
arrived with his wife and three children. A land mine had struck
the duplex house in which he lived and the building had collapsed to cellar level. His family, in the cramped little cellar, had
escaped unhurt.

It suddenly occurred to me that I had left in my room all the
personal luggage I had brought from Berlin: valuable family

papers, which I had intended to deposit in the country somewhere nearby, my stamp collection, my shotguns and hunting gear. I dashed across the short distance to the house, burst through the vestibule and into my room. The floor in the middle of the hall was already burning. I seized suitcase after suitcase as fast as I could and dragged them out to the main door. As I was rushing in for the third time a tongue of flame darted into my face. The only way in now was through the window. I clambered across the fallen rafters, got the bathroom window open, and climbed through. I threw everything I could get hold of into the open. Then I ran to my bedroom. The cupboard was in the alcove. I was going to save my hunting things and shotguns, at any rate. Just as I turned, with the shotguns under my arm, the door flew open with a loud crash. A huge darting flame shot through the antechamber and its glowing tentacles licked their way to bathroom and living room. Curtains and furniture were instantly ablaze. I was trapped in the alcove. Cursing and swearing, I dropped the shotguns, seized a blanket from the bed and wrapped myself in it. The burning furniture shone brightly in the hissing, all-devouring blaze that swept past me through the window. The heat became unbearable. The alcove curtains had caught fire.

Holding the blanket tightly round me with one hand, I involuntarily groped with the other for some object I might still be able to save. Then I dashed to the window and hurled myself out through the flames, throwing the blanket away as I fell.

Thank God! I was in the open.

As fast as I could I crawled on hands and knees out of range of the house. When I stood up I found I had saved the most absurd ashtray I had ever possessed. I threw it back.

Antiaircraft fire had ceased. An hour and a half had passed since the first bomb. I could hear the rattle of machine guns from the direction of the beach. Had our fighters turned up after all? The hum of the homeward-bound bombers' engines now sounded only faintly and at intervals against the crackling and crashing of the fires all round me.

The raid was over.

Worn out, I sat down for a moment on a filing cabinet and stared into the flames.

Hadn't I had a definite foreboding yesterday? The acrimonious dispute of the afternoon had not been the clearing storm. It occurred to me that my equanimity had been disturbed in the early morning by the replacement of heavy by medium AA guns, which had been carried out during the previous night without my knowledge.

I had received a warning from the Air Ministry a few days before that we were likely to be raided. We had also been warned by the reconnaissance aircraft that continuously flew over in fine weather. We had been prepared. At least one copy of all production blueprints, drawings, and files had been deposited elsewhere. Dispersal of the different departments was under way. All possible air-raid precautions had been taken.

The raid must have been a terrific one. Our carefully laid scheme, covering all eventualities and several times rehearsed, had failed completely. Now, two hours after the beginning, I still had no news from the other main targets. Some of the messengers had not got through. The dense fog, the destruction of the roads, rubble and fallen trees, had made it impossible to get cars or bicycles through to the south. I had sent the messengers out again on foot.

Here in the extreme north we had done all we could in the heat of the moment without any knowledge of the severity of the raid as a whole. Every available man had been in action. Reinforcements from the camps only three miles away, even if they walked, could not be much longer in coming.

"I've come from the settlement, sir. Volunteering for duty."

I looked up. Before me stood Becker, the assembly workshop overseer, panting, blackened, bathed in sweat.

"Thank God you've come! Sit down for a moment first. What's been happening in the settlement and at Karlshagen?"

"The settlement has been completely wiped out. It's ablaze from end to end. Land mines and sticks of bombs have practically flattened it. Over by the beach is supposed to be the worst."

"What about casualties?"

"I hope the slit trenches prevented their being too heavy."

"Tell me some names, man!"

"Doctor Thiel and Chief Engineer Walther were buried in one of the trenches. People were still digging for them when I left."

"Who else?"

"I came away at once, sir, to see what was happening to my workshop."

"Did you see the Pre-Production Works at all?"

"The administrative offices are on fire. I could see fires glowing in the windows of the big hall. The repair shop looked dark. I came straight through the woods. Fires everywhere, roads and railroad tracks completely wrecked. The by-pass road is chock-a-block with craters. What's been happening here? How's my assembly shop?"

"It's been hit rather badly. The stockrooms and extensions are on fire. One or two direct hits as well. But you'd better get your breath back. Then pick up anyone who's not too busy to help and see what you can save. Did you hear anything of the Labor Service or—"

He had already vanished into the fog.

One of the wardens came up and reported that no bombs had fallen on Peenemünde West.

Fischer, the canteen manager, suddenly appeared. He was hatless, in torn clothes, hurt and singed by phosphorus bombs. I told him to go and get coffee and soup ready at once.

At long last the leader of the Labor Service detachment arrived with his men. No casualties. Karlshagen camp, where about four thousand people were living, had been hit by only one bomb. Unluckily that had struck an accommodation barracks belonging to the Northern Experimental Command, and eight people had been killed.

I took the Labor Service major with me to the development works to see the component workshop. More and more engineers, soldiers, and workmen were coming in from the settlement and Karlshagen. One bearer of bad news followed another.

The wife and child of the chief warden on duty were among the dead. When he was told, he answered through clenched teeth, "I haven't time to listen now. We must save the works first."

I suddenly heard someone say, "Doctor Thiel, his whole family, and Chief Engineer Walther are dead."

I had been prepared for that. The loss was irreparable. Only now was I beginning to grasp the results of the raid. God grant it had not cost the lives of any more of my best people! The oldest members of our staff were living in the settlement.

Up here at the development works I had so far been told only of one death and several persons injured. I decided to go to the settlement and see for myself. I found von Braun and told him to take charge of the Station in my absence. I also told him to arrange for a "Storch" to be ready at 8 a.m. in the West Establishment, so that I could get an idea of the damage from the air.

It was still dark. Not a breath of wind stirred, and among the houses and trees fog, smoke, and fumes still lay suffocatingly on the chill morning air.

I took a bicycle and tried to get through. After a few yards I had to leave it in a ditch; the road was blocked by bomb craters. I stumbled over the torn-up rails and dangling wires of the electric railway into the dark woods filled with the acrid reek of burning.

I decided to go to the waterworks first. Our most urgent need for the day, especially if it were going to be so hot again, was water for drinking and cooking. The waterworks were undamaged. I went on to the big repair shop, used at that time as the assembly hall for experimental rockets. It was undamaged.

The farther south I penetrated, the more bomb craters I found. I noticed, however, that splinter damage, impeded by the soft sand of the dunes, had been slight. Then there rose before me, among the smoking, splintered trees, the big assembly hall of the Pre-Production Works. At first glance I could see no damage. I entered the place through the same small door by which I had left it the evening before, so full of happiness and confidence. The ground floor appeared to be intact. I went up one of the many concrete flights of steps leading to the great works hall. The early dawn light steeped the enormous, smoke-filled room in a livid glimmer, milkily pale. Nine 1000-pound bombs and many phosphorus and stick incendiaries had penetrated the concrete roof and exploded or burned out in that huge place. They were not able to cause much damage. Machines and materials had been hit by bomb splinters, there were hits in the outer side aisles, big holes in the masonry of the walls, but the damage was not really serious.

I hurried out of the hall in growing daylight and crossed the narrow strip of woods to the administrative buildings of the Pre-Production Works.

I stood still, breathless. In the big clearing beyond the wood the fog had vanished. The view was wide across a strangely altered landscape. Where were the barracks, the fire station, and Fischer's big canteen? Nothing remained but a mass of craters and smoking ruins. The finished wing of the great administrative building rose incredibly high above the flattened landscape. One could see right over to the settlement houses, smoking, glowing ruins, still blazing in places.

Tears of despair and rage came to my eyes as I gazed upon this spot, once so attractive and now churned and plowed by hundreds of bombs. I clambered wearily across the craters and ruins. Each step sent whirling aloft stifling clouds of dune sand, powdered by land mines to the finest possible dust.

At last I arrived at the settlement. Soldiers of the Northern Experimental Command, Labor Service men, and some of the staff were feverishly working to open up buried cellars, clear slit trenches, rescue furniture from burning houses, and remove fallen trees, beams, and other wreckage. I saw the bodies of men, women, and children. Some had been charred by phosphorus incendiaries. I learned that most families had fled along the coast to Zinnowitz while the raid was still on. I hurried along the beach road to Dr. Thiel's house. It had been destroyed by a direct hit. The slit trench in front was just a huge crater. I was told that Dr. Thiel's body had been laid out in the school.

I walked the short distance. Shaken to the very soul, I stood before the remains of Dr. Thiel, his wife, and his children. Poor, restless fellow, ever straining toward some new goal, filled with such enthusiasm and then with such despair! My heart overflowed with gratitude for all he had done for our project and for me. Two evenings before, in the evacuation officer's room, he had said, pale-faced and with absent eyes, these strangely prophetic words, "I shall never leave my wife and my children again while I live. They will stay here in the settlement with me."

My search for someone from the settlement administration took me to the old bathing beach at Karlshagen, at the southeast corner. My impression of horrible destruction deepened. The fine hostels for women employees, the administrative building, the houses and gardens, were all burned, bombed out and reduced to rubble, the earth torn up. Death had reaped a rich harvest here.

I pulled myself together. The most important thing now was to help the living. With this heart-rending scene of horror before me, I sent the first interim reports to Swinemünde, Stettin, and Berlin. By the time I returned to the staff building the first rescue parties were coming in from Wolgast, Anklam, Greifswald, and Swine-münde. I called an emergency conference for 11 a.m., and then made a survey trip by air with von Braun. On landing at 8:45, struck to the heart by this first comprehensive view of the destruction, I could only mutter wearily, "My poor, poor Peenemünde!" Not till several days later could we assess the size and tactics of the raid and the damage caused.

Six hundred four-engined British bombers are said to have taken part in the raid. According to the London radio, 1500 tons of high-explosive bombs and a huge number of incendiaries were dropped. Captured maps and sketches gave a clear idea of the plan of attack. The bombers had met over Rügen. After a diversionary maneuver by the first wave, designed to draw away fighter cover, they flew over Rügen from north to south straight to Peenemünde. Radar enabled them to ascertain exactly their range and main targets. The dense local smokescreen put up by Peene-münde was therefore useless. Fortunately the approach by air from Rügen to Peenemünde ran along the coast of Usedom, and a big proportion of the bombs fell on the dunes and into the sea, so that only the eastern part of the area was hit. The captured sketches showed the main targets to have been the test stands, the development works, the Pre-Production Works, the settlement, and the construction workers' camp at Trassenheide. The Air Force establishment at Peenemünde West was ignored, but the harbor sector, with its power station and oxygen plant, was marked as a fifth point of concentration.

The settlement was hit hardest. The British radio reports indicated that such was the intention. The scientists and technicians were known to live there.

Forty-seven bombers were shot down by AA guns and night fighters. It seems that the captured crews expressed astonishment at the relatively weak defenses. They had been thoroughly briefed and told that the attack would be one of the most important of the war, and that defenses were expected to be very strong; even if half the raiders were shot down and only the other half dropped their bombs the operation would be considered successful.

Serious damage to the works, contrary to first impressions, was surprisingly small. The test fields and such special installations as the wind tunnel and Measurement House were not hit at all. As a result of the immediate help given to us on a most generous scale, we were assured of being able to resume work after a delay of only four to six weeks. Moreover, by repairing only essential buildings, and by camouflage, we maintained the effect of complete destruction for nine months, during which we had no more raids. The project could not be prevented now from coming to fruition.

It was weeks before the exact number of casualties could be established. The raid had cost us 735 lives, including 178 of the 4000 inhabitants of the settlement. Losses were particularly heavy among foreign construction workers at Trassenheide camp.

CHAPTER 16

A TINY "T" ON AN AERIAL PHOTOGRAPH

From that memorable third of October, 1942, when our A-4 had performed perfectly for the first time, we had been convinced that the Allies would find us before very long. On clear days our tell-tale "frozen lightning" could be seen in the sky over Peenemünde from as far away as Sweden. Agents could call attention to us, and one day the keen eye of an Allied airborne camera would spot us. We had absolutely no illusions of what would follow then.

Since early in the spring of 1943 we had been expecting an air raid at any moment. At that time one of my employees thought that he had found the precise location and purpose of Peenemünde concealed in a crossword puzzle of a German illustrated paper. Though the Counterintelligence Section of the Army's High Command assured us that this was a minor matter, we maintained our vigilance.

Fate approached with an enervating and dangerous slowness. It took its time. When I use the term "enervating" I mean that in spite of the grease spots others claimed to see on the sleeves of our tunics we were still soldiers and knew very well indeed that our experiments could not have been unnoticed by the Allies. The question was merely "When"?

As military commander in charge I could not allow myself to be deceived by the general appearance of peace which seemed to pervade Peenemünde. Such constant alertness required a lot of nervous energy, also enormous quantities of camouflage material and time for daily checks and improvement of both camouflage and general air-raid precautions.

By the word "dangerous" I mean the danger that results when a large number of the employees arrives at the conclusion that everything is safe, with resultant carelessness. Practice alarms unfortunately have the result which is well exemplified by the story of the boy who cried "Wolf." False alarms cause wrong habits, they aid and abet a feeling of security, and then, one day . . .

I know now that only two months after the outbreak of the war, in the late fall of 1939, the British Government had received an anonymous but trustworthy and quite detailed report from Oslo in which it was stated that the Germans were experimenting on a large scale with large rockets and pilotless aircraft on a lonely island in the Baltic Sea.

What in fact did happen was that in the late fall of 1942 British Intelligence received with disturbing frequency reports of a secret long-range weapon capable of bombarding England from the Continent. No action was taken—then.

When, during the winter of 1942–43, reports about mysterious activities in the Peenemünde area piled up it became clear that something was going on there which, no matter how fantastic it sounded, demanded immediate investigation.

Mr. Duncan Sandys, at that time a member of the British War Cabinet, and Minister of Supply as I write, who was then and is now extremely interested in long-range rockets, began to check up on the truth and the implications of the agents' reports. After four weeks of the "wildest conjectures" he resolved to advise his Government to take serious notice of the rumors about German secret weapons. The RAF immediately began a new systematic air reconnaissance over the Continent. In time this developed into the greatest reconnaissance undertaking of the entire war.

Within a month an Intelligence officer working on a photograph in London found the first clue to the true significance of Peenemünde: the tiny shadow of a ramp, marked by a still tinier, bright T. For the first time the British saw a V-1. At the same time, Allied agents near Watten on the Channel coast were watching the rapid construction of a large and mysterious military installation. More of these were discovered as the summer went on, and the alarming suspicion arose that those installations must have something to do with the new secret weapon. To prevent its use at all costs, British and American squadrons made heavy and often blind attacks on these objectives.

These operations were given the code name "Crossbow" by Winston Churchill in December 1943. Later on, this designated all action taken by the Anglo-American Air Forces against the German long-range weapon program, its research and experimental stations, armament factories, and so on.

The first air raid on the big bunker at Watten on the French coast came only ten days after the attack on Peenemünde. Air reconnaissance soon discovered seven more large structures of a novel type, four in the Pas-de-Calais area and three at the tip of the Cherbourg peninsula. Two strangely shaped buildings were also discovered, each 100 yards long and resembling a pair of gigantic skis laid side by side, pointing in opposite directions. Twenty-one of these "ski sites" were found before the middle of November.

Prolonged and diligent observation of this sector of the French coast revealed a strange relationship among all the "ski sites": they all pointed toward London. British Intelligence had to conclude that this growing network of installations was to serve a long-range bombardment of London, headquarters of the forthcoming Allied invasion of the Continent. A few military and civilian experts tended to believe that all this might be a gigantic German swindle. It might all be intended just to frighten the Allies and persuade them not to try an invasion. But the majority of the scientists and engineers arrived at the opinion that the larger installations were take-off sites of gigantic rockets, and the smaller ones were launching ramps for small pilotless aircraft.

The mystery of these installations naturally caused all kinds of rumors. One was that the Germans were prepared to shoot large containers of "Red Death" to London. Another had it that the containers were filled with poison gas which would wipe out all life in the British Isles. Still another rumor stated that the Germans were preparing to produce artificial icebergs in the Channel and that they intended to blow clouds of ice crystals across the Channel to ground the bombardment squadrons.

On December 3, 1943, the Allies decided to destroy the installations covered by the code word Crossbow. This was not an easy decision to make because such a large, and in several respects uncertain, operation would occupy many of the bombardment squadrons which would otherwise be available for use against the German Air Force and German industry. Only a few hours after this decision had been reached an air reconnaissance of hitherto unparalleled intensity got under way. The whole coastline from Ostend to Cherbourg was minutely photographed; sixty-four "ski sites" were found within a week.

Attacks on the "ski sites" began December 5 but were at first greatly handicapped by bad weather. By the third week the number of "ski sites" found had risen to seventy-five. The Allies began to fear that the Germans might win the race for time. The first big blow was struck on Christmas Eve, 1943, when more than thirteen hundred American bombers attacked the installations all along the coast. But this attack did not yet settle matters. The Crossbow peril was anxiously discussed in London and Washington. The Allies were determined that, no matter what the cost, the planned invasion of the Continent should not be given up, or even postponed.

Secretary of War Henry L. Stimson formed a special committee of experts which was to study all reports and aerial photographs. The committee is said to have declared that the problem seemed insoluble unless there was a "lucky break" of some kind. Of course there were numerous suggestions, among them dropping poison gas on the "ski sites." Some even suggested not making the invasion across the Channel. Finally General Arnold suggested simply sending heavier and still heavier attacks against these mysterious installations. On January 12, 1944, General Marshall gave top priority to discovery of the best way to attack the Crossbow sites. The main responsibility for this lay with the Commanding Officer of the United States Air Force Experimental Station, Eglin Field, Florida.

Conventional methods would not do in a case of such urgency. On January 25, General Marshall put in a long-distance call from Washington to General Grandison Gardner, commander of Eglin Field. General Arnold was careful not to say clearly what he had in mind; he hoped that General Gardner would understand him just the same.

He said that there were one hundred and fifty of those things that look like skis on the northern French coast. "I want us to build some just like them. I will then attack these with new weapons. The work should be done in a few days, not weeks. It will take a lot of concrete. Top priority! And days, not weeks."

General Gardner immediately mobilized the resources of his enormous base and the thousands of men under his command. In the utmost secrecy the building activity so closely watched on the Channel coast was reproduced in the remote solitude of the tip of the Florida peninsula. The order read: Reproduction of the ski sites in complete detail and destruction in various ways.

Building materials were scarce or earmarked. But expediters found some somewhere in the United States. The materials were shipped to Eglin Field by airplane, train, truck, and steamer. Thousands of workers and soldiers built "ski sites" with steel, wood, brick, and concrete. They were then camouflaged and the picture rendered complete by the presence of antiaircraft artillery.

A few minutes after the concrete had hardened the replicas were attacked with every available weapon. The effect of each type of ammunition and of each kind of bombing was carefully observed by military and civilian experts. General Gardner reported results daily by telephone to General Arnold.

As soon as it was clearly established that one particular technique was superior to all the rest—low-level bombing by aircraft capable of dropping the heaviest bombs with the greatest accuracy on the most vulnerable point—General Gardner flew to England with a staff of officers from the Experimental Station to explain the method. The results were discussed with General Eisenhower and the leading British and American Air Force commanders. A film shot by Hollywood experts gave most of the onlookers their first idea of the appearance of the massive sites and of how they might best be destroyed.

While the Americans were convinced that it was now possible to eliminate the "ski sites" without weakening the air offensive over Germany, the British were skeptical. Differences of opinion arose. The nearer the invasion approached, the more strenuous grew the dispute.

Then Britain was startled by a new and alarming rumor. In February agents reported a new kind of structure, apparently intended as a launching site for the "Peenemünde flying configurations." These were of simple construction compared with the "ski sites." They were quickly built and camouflaged and constituted poor targets because they were so small. Meanwhile the Germans were using thousands of workmen to rebuild the giant structures and "ski sites" destroyed by bombing.

A few weeks before the invasion General Eisenhower ordered that until after heavy bombers had carried out a last large-scale operation on the launching sites, Crossbow should have top priority. The new small structures were not to be affected by this order. The invasion was to start on the appointed day, whatever Hitler might have in mind.

In May heavy bombers attacked for the last time before the invasion; on June 6 the invasion began; and on June 12 the first four V-1's flew to London. On the night of June 15 a new phase of the war opened, the battle of the flying bombs, which did not end until March 1945.

General Eisenhower said in *Crusade in Europe* [1]:

"It seemed likely that, if the German had succeeded in perfecting and using these new weapons six months earlier than he did,

[1] Doubleday & Co., New York, 1948; page 260.

our invasion of Europe would have proved exceedingly difficult, perhaps impossible. I feel sure that if he had succeeded in using these weapons over a six-month period, and particularly if he had made the Portsmouth-Southampton area one of his principal targets, Overlord might have been written off."

CHAPTER 17

HITLER MAKES
A WRONG DECISION

Shortly after the raid on Peenemünde the factories at Friedrichs-hafen and Weiner Neustadt, both earmarked for production, were also attacked. The big firing bunker at Watten suffered a heavy raid at a critical stage in its erection and was left a fantastic heap of wet concrete, steel, and lumber. The concrete hardened. After a few days the bunker was beyond salvage. All we could do was roof in a part and use it for other work.

We had had the foresight to choose an alternative location not far from Watten, a big limestone pit near Wizernes, where there was to be a large underground dump for finished rockets.

Dorsch, the new head of the Todt organization, thought he could save a section of the bunker, about 300 feet wide by 150 long. He suggested a remarkable new idea for doing this. The walls, 15 feet thick and at the moment 12 feet high, would be immediately roofed with concrete 10 feet thick. This roof, weighing thousands of tons, would be bodily lifted in stages by hy-draulic means and the walls built up beneath it. Once the struc-ture was the right height we could think of increasing the thick-ness of the roof to the 23 feet prescribed by Hitler.

Watten was of course useless now as a launching site, but the bunker could still be used for an oxygen-liquefaction plant. Dorsch suggested we should go into this at Peenemünde and draw up new plans.

At Wizernes, now earmarked as our launching site, Dorsch

intended to use a different method: placing a dome of concrete 20 feet thick on the top of the quarry. The quarry would then be hollowed out from within and the dome provided with pillar supports. As the stone was loose and crumbly this would be an extremely risky business, but Dorsch considered it the only way to get the building done in view of the intensified bombing. In both cases he intended to begin with the protective roof and continue the work underneath.

Dorsch did not want to take sole responsibility for two such extensive building schemes. He sought a decision from Hitler, and I was summoned to the Führer's headquarters. I traveled by rail.

There was another reason for my visit. For some weeks my department had been seeking clear terms of reference for our part in the A-4 program from General Buhle at headquarters. Unfortunately, however, the draft finally worked out by General Jodl dealt only with the purely military aspects. My staff had been put in charge of preparations for action throughout France. Therefore the relation of my department to the Commander-in-Chief of the western front in Paris, Field Marshal von Rundstedt, had to be made quite clear. I was to represent the Armed Forces High Command in France and receive my orders direct from that body. At home, however, I should still be subordinate to the Commander-in-Chief of the Home Front, Colonel General Fromm. The order to this effect was to be signed by Hitler during my forthcoming audience.

The conference took place in Hitler's study. Keitel, Jodl, Buhle, Dorsch, and a stenographer were present.

We sat down at the big round conference table. This time I saw Hitler in clear daylight and was again shocked at his appearance. He seemed to me to have aged still more since our last meeting on July 7. I particularly noticed the unhealthy, yellowish, not to say greenish-yellow, color of his complexion and soft hands. Against the ghastly pallor of his face, tiny, dark-red veins made shadowy patches round the big nose.

I sat on Hitler's left. To begin with, he was as silent and preoccupied as always. Jodl opened the proceedings. I had been earnestly advised to raise no objections and told that the order as drafted was the most that could be offered me.

Hitler signified his agreement.

I wondered then, and I still wonder today, why the powers given to us soldiers in the Third Reich tied rather than freed our hands. Why were we not trusted, why were we not given authority to act on our own judgment? Why was it that the SS, the Ministry of Munitions, and the Party got everything they wanted? Was the service itself to blame for its internal rivalries, quarrels over jurisdiction, and reluctance to take responsibility? Or had people simply resigned themselves to the accepted fact of Hitler's now permanent distrust of the Army? When Jodl pushed the document across the table and the stenographer placed pen and ink ready, Hitler put on spectacles. They were ordinary cheap spectacles with metal rims and a narrow metal bridge. It was the first time I had seen the Supreme War Lord wear glasses. Had he become far-sighted? His hand trembled slightly as he scrawled his illegible signature, beginning with a flourish and tailing off to nothing, on the three copies of the order.

Then Dorsch began to speak. Hitler at once brightened up. Speer had told me that he always sat up and took notice whenever anyone mentioned a building scheme. He was immediately captured by the grandiose plans Dorsch described and had them all explained in detail, after which he enthusiastically consented.

I could not remain silent. I considered it my duty to point out that there would be more air attacks on Watten. Now the place had been identified it would certainly not be allowed to go on working undisturbed.

Dorsch replied that the existing mess on the site would not be cleared up; from the air it would look like a destroyed and abandoned station. However, I felt it important to put Hitler off this bunker idea altogether and described in emphatic terms the advantages of putting the A-4 into action from motorized batteries. Hitler heard me out but gave his decision in favor of Dorsch.

The two building projects were begun but never finished.

Hitler's faulty decision was due to his enthusiasm for building and his failure to understand the air situation in the West. It caused valuable building materials and labor to be diverted for months to a task which could never be completed.

The site at Watten was actually roofed in and the first stage of building finished without serious interruption, but at that point the heavy 6-ton bombs came into action. True, they were unable to penetrate the concrete roof, but they dug into the ground near the bunker and tilted the machinery foundations, making the bunker useless.

At Wizernes, too, the big concrete dome was successfully placed in position, but persistent air attack with heavy and superheavy bombs so battered the rock all round it that in the spring of 1944 landslides made further work impossible.

The writing was now on the wall in letters of glowing flame: those fateful words, "Too late," that had dogged our work all through the war.

CHAPTER 18

A NEW POWER COMES
TO THE FORE

At the beginning of April 1943 the Reichsführer SS, Heinrich Himmler, visited Peenemünde for the first time. The unexpected announcement of his visit caused Colonel General Fromm and the head of the Army Weapons Department, General Leeb, to put in an appearance too.

We were not able to fire an A-4 that day and had to convey an idea of the work we were doing by lectures and demonstrations of static tests.

This was my first real sight of Himmler. Going round with him, and talking to him in the mess, I tried in vain to find in his appearance, behavior, and conversation that inexplicable, exciting, and mysterious quality which had made him one of the most hated and feared of Hitler's close associates in the eyes of the world.

He looked to me like an intelligent elementary-school teacher, certainly not like a man of violence. I could not for the life of me see anything outstanding or extraordinary about this middle-sized, youthfully slender man in SS uniform. Under a brow of average height two gray-blue eyes, behind glittering pince-nez, looked at me with an air of peaceful interrogation. The trimmed mustache below the straight, well-shaped nose traced a dark line on his unhealthily pale features. The lips were colorless and very thin. Only the inconspicuous, receding chin surprised me. The skin of his neck was flaccid and wrinkled. With a broadening of his constant set smile, faintly mocking and sometimes contemptuous about the corners of the mouth, two rows of excellent white teeth appeared between the thin lips. His slender, pale, and almost girlishly soft hands, covered with blue veins, lay motionless on the table throughout our conversation.

I told him about our development work and future plans. He listened with interest, now and then putting a question. Suddenly he began to explain the reason for the visit which had so surprised us all.

He said that recently we had been much talked about in the Führer's intimate circle. We were right in the limelight. He had therefore wished to find out what was being done at Peenemünde and how he could best employ his powers on our behalf. "Once the Führer has decided," he continued, "to give your project his support, your work ceases to be the concern of the Army Weapons Department, or indeed of the Army at all, and becomes the concern of the German people. I am here to protect you against sabotage and treason."

I made an effort to repress the uneasiness which these words produced in me. Colonel General Fromm, sitting on Himmler's other side, interposed courteously, but with a slight flush of resentment, "Reichsführer, Peenemünde is an Army establishment. In an Army establishment the Army alone is responsible for security. I should, however, welcome your declaration of a prohibited zone round Peenemünde and a tightening up of security measures in northern Usedom and the adjacent mainland."

After a short silence Himmler agreed and delegated the task to the police commissioner for Stettin, SS General Mazuw, who was present.

As I was taking leave of Himmler later beside his airplane at Peenemünde West, he said, "I am extremely interested in your work. I may be able to help you. I will come again alone and spend the night here, and we can have a private talk with your colleagues. I will telephone you."

A week later one of my section chiefs, Air Staff Engineer Zeyss, back from Brünn, told me that SS officers there were openly saying that I was the brake on rocket development in Germany. If it had not been for me, they said, we should have been much further by this time. The loudest voice had been that of SS Captain Engel, who had earlier worked for a short time at the Raketenflugplatz in Berlin and was now in charge of an SS rocket-research station at Grossendorf, near Danzig.

I had been inured for many years to criticism of every kind, but such open and specific accusations could be very dangerous to our work and aims at a moment when the SS were infiltrating more and more into weapon development. I reported the matter to my Service chief, who advised me to be very careful.

A few days later I invited the head of the Development Branch of the SS Weapons Department, General Gärtner, as well as SS Captain Engel, to pay me a visit, and asked for enlightenment. The visitors showed embarrassment and could give me no definite information. In the end I decided to give them a general idea of the work my department had done on rockets since 1930. They listened in astonishment, apologized, and assured me they had had no conception of most of it.

I realized clearly enough that this was only the beginning of new battles. My Service chief advised me to prepare a memorandum to arm myself against further attacks. I wrote a long treatise entitled *Rocket Development: The Achievement of the Army Weapons Department, 1930–1943*, and had it printed at Peenemünde.

The second blow was struck on April 26, 1943. Just before 6 o'clock in the evening the adjutant of the Army Weapons Department telephoned and requested me to tell Colonel Zanssen, station commander at Peenemünde for many years, that he was relieved of his duties immediately. He was to leave Peenemünde that same day. The order had come through by telephone from the head of the Personnel Office at Hitler's headquarters. Horrified, I asked the reason. The adjutant said there seemed to be some dispute with the SS; that was all they had been able to find out.

I rang up Zanssen at once and told him that he must leave immediately for a conference in Berlin. An hour or two later he called at my private house. I asked him whether he knew anything about a quarrel with the SS. He couldn't make head or tail of it. He told me that until the start of discussions about the prohibited zone he had never had anything to do with the SS. The dealings with SS Lieutenant Colonel Müller had gone without a hitch. I then revealed to him that he was to be relieved forthwith. Naturally enough he was extremely upset, and I had much difficulty in persuading him to go to bed.

Next morning I reported to Colonel General Fromm. He was enraged at the manner in which the order had been issued and detailed me, as Zanssen's superior officer, to investigate the matter.

I next approached Colonel Schniewind of the Personnel Office, who handled our staff questions, and asked him to give me some documentation for the order I had received to relieve Zanssen. He told me he had nothing apart from the headquarters order passed to him by Major General Linnartz. I urged him to do what he could to hurry procedure along.

At a friend's house that evening I was told that some days before, when Zanssen's name was mentioned at a party, a senior official of the Ministry of Munitions had remarked that the balloon would go up at Peenemünde any day now. First Zanssen would go, and I would follow a few days later.

Thus a new and powerful office hitherto unnoticed by us, that of Himmler, had intervened in the battle about jurisdiction over Peenemünde.

A few days later I received from the Personnel Office a copy of a letter to the Personnel Office chief, signed by Himmler. This letter contained childish accusations against Zanssen, which could be refuted immediately by anyone in possession of the facts. Himmler went on to say that he had not been able to check these charges but considered that the Personnel Office should be aware of them. In his opinion the retention of Zanssen at Peenemünde in these circumstances could not be tolerated.

As Peenemünde could not be left without a station commander at this critical period I had to take over from Zanssen in addition to my other duties and transfer my office to Peenemünde. Zanssen temporarily represented me in Berlin. Within a few days I had finished my report, which showed the charges to be utterly without foundation. All I needed to complete it was conclusive evidence on letters alleged to have been written by Zanssen.

The Zanssen case was being handled by an SS office controlled by SS General Berger. I went to see him. Berger was a squat, powerfully built, dark-haired South German with piercing black eyes. The following conversation took place.

"General," I began, "I have been ordered by Colonel General Fromm to investigate the case of Colonel Zanssen, station commandant at Peenemünde. I assume you know of it?"

Berger nodded in corroboration. I went on, "All I need now is a deposition from the man who laid the information. Colonel Zanssen is an officer of proved excellence in the front line and at home. If such a serious step as sudden dismissal is to be justified I must examine the grounds. May I therefore ask you in the interests of justice to give me the name of this man?"

Berger replied, "I am not going to give you the name."

I understood. The whole thing was a farce and not even a very clever one. "That's very regrettable," I retorted. "I should have been glad to know who was behind the charges, and particularly whether the complaint belongs to Peenemünde. Apart from that, however, it has been clearly proved by sworn testimony that the accusations against Colonel Zanssen are quite without foundation. My only other request is to be allowed to see the letters you are said to have from Zanssen, to clear up this last point."

Berger asked to see the file. I handed it over. After briefly glancing through it he returned it to me with the remark, "Although it may seem from these papers as though you might be right on many points, I can't give you the letters." I had expected that.

"General," I said, "have you got the letters?"

"Yes."

"Then will you let me examine them here in your presence?"

"No!" Berger snapped back. "I'm not going to let you handle those letters!"

I refused to give in. "Then will you at least allow me to glance at them, so that I can see whether they are in Colonel Zanssen's handwriting, which I know, or are forgeries?"

Our voices were growing steadily sharper and colder.

"No!" Berger's tone was conclusive. "I won't do that either."

I resigned myself. "Then, General, you will understand that for the purposes of my investigation the letters have no existence."

"You are at liberty to assume anything you please," Berger retorted icily. I left the room.

Since the investigation had shown the charges to be unfounded Colonel General Fromm decided that Colonel Zanssen should take over Peenemünde again in the late autumn. He informed Himmler of this decision in a very cold letter. This seemed to settle the wretched business for the time being, even if we did not get full satisfaction. Nevertheless, the threat of a formidable power working behind the scenes remained. Himmler was not likely to forget his defeat. Nor did he. Nearly eighteen months went by, there were fresh intrigues, and finally the Army Weapons Department, tired of the battle, ordered Zanssen to the front, thus depriving our organization of one of its most loyal and deserving members.

Not until after the war did I learn the kind of tactics that were used against the commander of Peenemünde, a strictly Army establishment. Himmler had summoned Dr. von Braun to his headquarters and sworn him to secrecy. Himmler then asked him with cynical frankness how he would react if the SS took over Peenemünde, remarking that he could not imagine that the Army could offer von Braun anything like the same scope as the SS could. Von Braun politely but firmly rejected this suggestion, leaving no doubt that he would have nothing to do with any such intrigue and would inform his superior officers if necessary.

CHAPTER 19

HIMMLER EXPLAINS THE WAR

Himmler announced that his second visit to Peenemünde would take place on June 29. By the afternoon of that day Mazuw, the police commissioner of Stettin, and SS Lieutenant Colonel Müller had already arrived. They said they didn't want to bother me and went into Fischer's canteen. However, I wanted to discuss the Zanssen affair with them and sent a request that they should come and see me. At the interview I thought they seemed embarrassed and I don't believe I was mistaken. I asked them straight out to tell me on their honor whether they had any knowledge of the Zanssen affair. They denied knowing anything at all about it. There was nothing more to be got out of them. I determined to ask Himmler himself.

Toward evening Himmler arrived at Peenemünde unaccompanied, driving his private little armored car. After a modest evening meal with a few of my colleagues he dismissed the SS people from Stettin, and we went to sit in the Hearth Room. Colonel Stegmaier, Ministerial Councilor Schubert, Professor von Braun, Rees, Steinhoff, and a few senior members of the staff were present.

Conversation dragged at first. I was several times tempted to bring up Zanssen's name but in the end postponed the idea until the following morning, when I hoped to have a chance of speaking to Himmler alone.

Von Braun told Himmler of our beginnings at Kummersdorf. He described our hopes and aims and managed to convey that here at Peenemünde we were solidly united against any kind of obstacle. The talk then shifted to the subject of our worries. At

that time Hitler's recognition of us was still in the balance. We
mentioned how anxiously we were awaiting inclusion in the top
priority group. Everyone was soon taking part in the conversation and describing his own field of activity and ambitions. The
hours slipped by. We talked about the prospects of space travel
and the steps toward its realization.

Himmler possessed the rare gift of attentive listening. Sitting
back with legs crossed, he wore throughout the same amiable and
interested expression. His questions showed that he grasped un-
erringly what the technicians told him out of their wealth of
knowledge. The talk turned to the war and the important questions in all our minds. He answered without hesitation, calmly
and candidly. It was only at rare moments that, sitting with his
elbows resting on the arms of the chair, he emphasized his words
by tapping the tips of his fingers together. He was a man of quiet,
unemotional gestures, a man without nerves. Himmler talked
of high politics. He repeated the old phrases, so familiar on the
radio and in the press, which had been hammered into all our
heads. For quite a while I only half listened. We engineers were
not used to political talk and found it difficult. But since the
subject had come up, and we had someone with us who must
assuredly know all about it, I put the great, fundamental question
to him, "Reichsführer, what are we really fighting for?"

Himmler replied without hesitation, "The Führer thinks and
acts for the benefit of Europe. He regards himself as the last
champion of the Western world and its culture. He is convinced
that modern achievements in technology, especially railroad,
highway, and air transport, have made national boundaries un-
important and obsolete. Small nations not economically self-
sufficient must join more powerful ones. In modern conditions
only economic units of great size can survive, those politically
and productively strong enough to assert their independence.

"Europe, by reason of its history, its geographical position,
its economic structure, and its share of raw materials, is such a
unit. The European area must form a group, with the power that
is economically and politically strongest as its nucleus. For their

own benefit the nations must voluntarily subordinate themselves
to the leadership of this strongest state. If we are not to lose our
European standards of living and our economic status, this large
unit must come into being sooner or later. The only question is:
which nation shall assume the leadership? The Führer believes
that only a racially sound Germany, economically stable, patrioti-
cally united, and politically strong, is preordained to do so."

I was familiar with this line of thought. However, I wanted
to know more about it. "But surely," I continued, "these considerations were bound to involve us in conflict with nations unwilling
to resign their independence, and with the other great powers of
the world?"

Himmler nodded. He resumed, "The Führer was aware from
the beginning that the world would not tolerate a stronger Germany, much less a Europe under German leadership. Wealthy
nations will always try to prevent the rise of a poor relation. That
is only human nature. England, because of her geographical
position, is exposed to great centrifugal forces—that is, her interests lie too much overseas for her ever to be able to assume European leadership. Despite this the Führer tried to come to an
understanding with England. His desire was for a division of tasks
between the two peoples. His efforts failed. Yet he has still not
given up hope that the Anglo-Saxons will one day see reason, or
see, rather, where their own advantage lies."

He said this in June 1943!

"In the Führer's view," continued Himmler in his calm, even
tones, "a European economic unit under Anglo-German leadership would not necessarily conflict with the interests of American
economic policy."

I mentioned Russia.

"Russia," Himmler responded, "ought not to be considered in
isolation. The other Slav peoples in Europe must be included. If
Russia ever succeeds in welding together the Slav bloc of three
hundred million people, industrializing them and turning them
into fanatics, it will be all over with Western predominance.

This danger threatening the Western world and its culture from the east was one of the reasons for the war with Russia."

I asked, "Is it your view, then, that the economic danger threatening us from the east is so formidable?"

Himmler's reply was almost automatic. "The Western worker is highly qualified but he is demanding and, racially speaking, tired. He wants to get something out of life. At the end of his eight-hour working day he wants to enjoy his home, his family, his leisure, and his garden. Wages are correspondingly high. To some extent he regards his job in the factory as only a means to an end, a way of enabling him to lead a carefree life after his work is over. He wants to share in the cultural achievements of his age.

"Not so the Russian worker. He is comparatively new to industrial work. He is fresh, enthusiastic, good with his hands, not worn out or spoiled by outside pleasures, because his life apart from the factory can offer him nothing worth living for. Like the Japanese worker, he is the cheapest kind of labor a highly developed industry could wish for. The Russian government has been highly successful at teaching the Russian worker to enjoy industrial work. It offers him in the factories all the social and cultural advantages lacking in his home. By keeping his domestic standard of living at a low level it compels him to work harder in the factory of his own accord. The Russian worker loves his factory. The day is bound to come when Stalin, unless we stop him, will switch industry from armaments to consumer goods. In view of the complete nationalization of Russian industry he is free to take any line he pleases in this. Russia will then be able to flood world markets with extremely cheap goods. The world would have no answer to this, especially if such economic expansion were backed by great military force. The consequence would be economic catastrophe in Western Europe and America, and the chief victims would be the workers."

I asked, "Then our war aims in Russia are economic rather than military or political, or, say, ideological?"

Himmler smiled ironically. "In the last analysis every war is a struggle for power. In modern wars all three factors are invariably involved."

Finally conversation turned to policy in the east after the war, Poland under the "General Government." Himmler's glasses glittered. Was I mistaken, or had his imperturbable, impenetrable mask of amiability fallen a little? Could he feel certain reservations in my carefully phrased inquiries?

"What else could we have done?" he proceeded. "You must always remember that the thickly populated soil of Germany can support only about sixty per cent of its inhabitants. The resources required for maintaining the standard of living for all of us, and for supporting the balance of forty per cent, must be imported. The Führer calculates that the population of Germany will be one hundred million in ten years. The problem of food supply urgently needs solution. The Führer regards himself as a Western European. He sees the danger as coming from the east. He has no desire to extend westward. In order to preserve Western Europe he needs strong and civilized peoples behind him. The only possible means of ensuring the support and settlement abroad of our overflowing population, particularly if the Western powers maintain their present economic policy, are to be found in the thinly populated lands to the east."

I objected, "The lands to the east are certainly thinly populated at the moment. But do you believe that those lands, in view of their tremendous annual increase of population, could be settled permanently with Germans and preserved for the German people? The attempt to do so has already failed twice."

Himmler's answer was, "Obviously a fall in the birth rate over there will have to be brought about in some way. I am myself in charge of planning for colonization. We have enough settlers. If the second and third sons of our land-owners and farmers in the east are settled in groups at first to form a series of population centers, and every official has to do a spell of duty in the east, we can expand from these centers and eventually secure the land permanently for Germany."

My next question was, "Are you sure the German will be equal to the climate in the long run?"

Himmler's fingertips beat lightly against one another. "We shall arrange for the young German peasants to marry Ukrainian girls of good farming stock and found a healthy new generation adapted to conditions out there."

"Won't other nations stigmatize this expansion eastward as an injustice that cries to high heaven, and the subjugation of foreign peoples as a return to the age of slavery?" I dared to ask.

"If the war is won they will beware of doing so. Besides, our intention is at first to use no more force than we need to get a start. We must practice a rigid state-planned economy with both men and material throughout conquered territory. But the more it gets going, the more a certain stability is achieved, the more goods are produced and distributed, by so much more will the standard of living of the individual rise, especially that of the unskilled and lower-paid worker in the countries of the European economic unit. I am convinced that a free plebiscite, taken after a few years, would register a hundred per cent agreement with German policy."

I did not know whether the ideas expressed by Himmler were his own or whether he was merely repeating what he had heard. This unlimited supply of ideas, plans, and projects, so monstrous to the ears of us laymen, this revolting policy of violence, was so concisely, simply, and naturally presented that it might well have originated with that great simplifier, Hitler himself. I shuddered at the everyday manner in which the stuff was retailed. But even as I did so I admired Himmler's gift for expressing difficult problems in a few words that went straight to the heart of the matter, and could be understood by anyone.

I was reminded of a well-known remark of Hitler's to a lieutenant colonel of the Army Weapons Department on his first visit to Kummersdorf in October 1933. The colonel had been explaining some problem with very long-winded erudition. Hitler interrupted him. "I will now tell you in a few words what you've been trying to say all this time." And he did so.

We hardly ever discussed politics in Peenemünde. We were out of the world. Whenever two people met in the canteen or at mess, their conversation would turn within five minutes to valves, relay contacts, mixers, supplementary resistance factors, or some other technical detail that was giving us trouble. If directors were gathered together over drinks or at bowling it was worse still. If you talk shop in an officers' mess the steward is normally told to bring a pair of fatigue-dress trousers and hang them up over the table. By the same token we ought to have had a riveting hammer or electrical steering gear as a permanent feature. Almost all our daily lives, our thoughts and aspirations, had been revolving for years about the development of our A-4. Our work had made us sober realists. We knew how dangerous it was to let ideas and plans run too far into the future.

I now put the question which had been exercising me. "Does the Führer believe that we have enough men and materials to carry out such a tremendous task, now that we are up against the armament potential of the entire world?"

Himmler seemed to have been expecting this question. "As I told you, the Führer regards himself as the champion of Europe against the danger from the east. Because of this he is convinced that Europe, while perhaps leaving the Germans to fight alone, must at least help them economically. In his view large parts of Europe have not seen the immediate danger and therefore oppose him. We must bear in mind the greatness of our mission and simply force people to accept their good fortune. European industry must work for the great cause. The whole wealth of labor we now control must be enlisted in the life-and-death struggle."

A monstrous demand! How could it possibly be realized?

"Reichsführer, for reasons of security I have never yet employed foreign labor for my work. I cannot think that our industry would gain much by using it on a big scale. In the Berlin subway nowadays you hear practically nothing but French or some Eastern language. The danger of sabotage and spying in armament factories seems to me immense."

Himmler's permanent smile seemed to deepen. "Sabotage can be eliminated by employing German overseers. Spying can be reduced to a minimum by close supervision and severe punishments. The call for mobilization of European labor for Europe's life-and-death struggle against the barbarism of the Asiatic steppes has already persuaded a great mass of people to work for us voluntarily. In my view the prospect of high wages and good food in Germany, or in foreign industry under German control, will induce even more Europeans to join in the work. The Führer is of the opinion that as a result the economic potential of Germany combined with European industry will balance the enemy's."

Hours and hours had passed. The topic now became the great men of history. Tired as I was, my interest revived when Himmler told us that Hitler considered Stalin to be his only really great adversary. Great? What did that mean? Himmler gave the word equal significance in connection with the negative, destructive, and ruinous. He recalled Genghis Khan, who had certainly been the most feared and abominated man of his time, yet history had not denied his qualities as a great general and statesman. Despite his failure to consolidate Mongol predominance in Asia beyond his own lifetime, his unique and meteoric career, the ruthlessness of his politics, and the ferocity of his armies had left his mark for centuries on the face of the Asiatic world and much of Europe. In this connection Himmler enlarged on the modern rulers of Russia, in whom he claimed to find undoubted traces of the old Mongol warriors. He reminded us that descendants of the Golden Horde are still to be found in Central Russia. The characteristic features of Russian psychology, he maintained, come from that source: sophisticated cunning, amazing physical toughness, incomprehensible cruelty, the wildest fanaticism, contempt of death, indifference to hardship and disaster, and resignation in the face of conditions which to us appear subhuman. Himmler thought that only Asiatic methods would make any impression on such a mentality, utterly opposed as it was to that of the Western European. No other attitude would be understood by a Russian.

Toward 4 o'clock in the morning I finally pleaded for a break-up of the meeting. Despite the late hour I lay awake for a long time, pondering over what I had heard. All those ideas never thought out to their logical conclusion, all those apparently reasonable theories created to justify an inhuman policy of force, troubled me exceedingly. Out of all I had heard during those long hours how much was honest conviction, how much propaganda, and how much true?

Next morning our first launching miscarried. The A-4, the moment it rose, began turning about its longitudinal axis and did not answer the steering commands. It assumed a nearly horizontal position and flew at barely 600 feet in the diametrically wrong direction over the woods toward Peenemünde West. After a few seconds' flight it came down on the airfield there. A dense black cloud of smoke shot with flame rose high above the woods. As it changed to a gigantic, threatening mushroom the air was filled with a thunderous roar. Nearly 8 tons of fuel had exploded on impact. Even here, 2 miles away, the windows rattled.

At Peenemünde West, where I arrived with Himmler in my car a few minutes later, people were dashing hither and thither like distracted ants. Windowpanes were out everywhere. We drove on along the concrete road to the airfield.

Luckily no one had been injured. The yawning crater, nearly 100 feet in diameter and rapidly filling with water, was a few hundred yards from the nearest hangar. Blackish fragments of earth from the subsoil, mingled with the white sand of the airport, covered the green grass over a wide area round the crater. Three aircraft had been destroyed by blast and lay twisted and gaping, as though struck down by a giant's fist. Once more, as so often before, we had been lucky in misfortune. It was very nearly a miracle that in all our years at Peenemünde we had not lost a single man through the rocket itself. There had been automobile accidents and injuries through carelessness, but a kindly fate had preserved us so far from serious mishaps.

The second launching was scheduled for the afternoon. We took advantage of the fine summer weather to cross over to the

Greifswalder Oie for lunch in one of our search motor launches.
As the boat left the Peene and made for the open Baltic, I had
a chance at last of speaking to Himmler in private. We stood together on the foredeck, looking over the railing into the milky
haze beyond which lay the blue-gray silhouette of the Oie.

After more discussion of why the rocket had failed, I came to
the matter which had been worrying me for months. I asked the
reason for Zanssen's dismissal. Himmler's manner became icy.
At first he declared that he did not remember the case. When I
pressed him, and stressed the injustice that had been done, he
stared straight ahead across the sea and answered after a brief
pause, "You had better rest content with the fact that Colonel
General Fromm is reinstating Colonel Zanssen. So far as you
are concerned that surely closes the incident."

"For me perhaps," I admitted, "but not for Zanssen by any
means."

After a pause he remarked testily, "Let us talk of something
else."

I had learned nothing which could throw any light on the matter. It was still in the balance. The danger had not been averted.

In the afternoon the second launching of the A-4 went off without a hitch. Himmler then took his leave. He promised to present
our point of view to Hitler, adding that he could help us only
if Hitler's decision were favorable.

CHAPTER 20

THE "ORGANIZATION"

Early in September 1943, soon after the raids on our intended centers of production, a new name appeared on our program. Himmler had appointed SS Brigadier Dr. Kammler, head of the building branch of the SS Head Office, to take charge of building needed for production under the A-4 special committee of the Ministry of Munitions. The efficiency of the program hitherto entirely run by the Army had already been vitiated by the introduction of the special committee subordinate to the Ministry of Munitions. What was the idea of splitting the program still further by appointing a "commissioner" directly responsible to Himmler?

It was simply that a phenomenon which by this time was a matter of course in the armaments industry had now extended to the A-4. New organizations were springing up like mushrooms after rain alongside the old and tried ones and inflating themselves furiously. In most cases there was overlapping if not actual duplication. All the departmental bosses, out of suspicion, lust for power, or sheer obstinacy, then jealously fought for independence. Occasionally a new organization with few but able men in it had the drive to score a certain initial success. This, it alleged, justified its existence and even entitled it to expand. In no time it grew just as cumbersome and hidebound as the predecessors or competitors which it claimed had been failures.

In the spring of 1943, at Hitler's orders, General von Unruh had visited home establishments, including the Army Weapons Department. His orders were to eliminate all fit men not engaged on essential war work, cut down civil-service establishments, and abolish any redundant departments. In a conference at the Army

Weapons Department he said to its chief, "At my last visit you outlined the duties of your department and gave reasons for maintaining such a big staff. Well, I have just found exactly similar jobs being done at the Ministry of Munitions. Work is being duplicated here. Can you account for that?"

General Leeb, though the twitching of the wrinkles at the corners of his eyes revealed an inward smile, answered with a straight face, "The explanation is very simple. If an invention comes off or the goods are delivered in any way, the Ministry of Munitions claims the credit. If it doesn't come off, the Army Weapons Department gets the blame. In either case the work is done by my department."

I don't know whether General von Unruh was convinced by this argument, but at any rate the cut in the staff of the Army Weapons Department remained at 20 per cent as previously fixed.

To get over the increasing confusion, red tape, and interdepartmental quarrels, an attempt was made in important cases, or where profit seemed to be involved, to appoint special commissioners who were to put business through ruthlessly without regard to channels. Nobody realized that these special commissioners were bound to collide with one another at one of the bottlenecks then common to all the undertakings—vacuum tubes, rare metals, or specialists.

As suspicion, envy, jealousy, and the itch for independence continued to reign, every head of an organization, obstinately determined to be in the swim and get talked about, now appointed deputies of his own, directly responsible to himself, in the fields that particularly interested him. His motive was, of course, purely the desire to help. The recipient of the alleged help remained in charge—on paper. He was befogged and lulled by benevolent phrases, such as "Under your management, of course," "In accordance with your memoranda and your ideas"; "In the closest and most loyal collaboration"; "Come and see me if you don't get on together"; and similar eyewash.

But these commissioners belonging to the different organizations were generally very tough eggs, as was to be expected from the nature of their appointments. They could rarely be induced to change their preconceived opinions by discussion or appeals to reason. When five or six men of this type were engaged on a program whose "director" had no power of decision, there was bound to be trouble, even if there had been the best will in the world.

In no time differences of opinion arose, and since responsibility was so ill defined, suspicion developed which damped enthusiasm. Then came verbal gauntlets, such as: "I don't care what you say, I shall act as I have told you"; "I don't take orders from you; you are not my superior"; "The decision rests with my superior officers"; "I must send in a report on that and get a decision."

The result was intrigue and intensified struggles for power. Higher levels were drawn into the conflict. Decisions were finally taken, to the accompaniment of peppery observations on the inefficiency of the other parties concerned, not so much by the most competent authority as by the most powerful one—by the man who could rely on support in high places.

It was on September 6, 1943, while on a duty trip to Berlin, that I first met Dr. Kammler, the new commissioner for building.

He had the slim figure of a cavalryman, neither tall nor short. In his early forties, broad-shouldered and narrow in the hips, with bronzed, clear-cut features, a high forehead under dark hair slightly streaked with gray and brushed straight back, Dr. Kammler had piercing and restless brown eyes, a lean, curved beak of a nose, and a strong mouth, the underlip thrust forward as though in defiance. That mouth indicated brutality, derision, disdain, and overweening pride. The chin was well molded and prominent.

One's first impression was of a virile, handsome, and captivating personality. He looked like some hero of the Renaissance, a *condottiere* of the period of the civil wars in northern Italy. The mobile features were full of expression. But the hands were thick and soul-less, almost coarse.

It was not long before I had a clear idea of the man's character. After a few moments he captured the conversation. There was nothing to do but to let him talk. His first concern was to show you what a splendid fellow he was, how boldly he spoke his mind to his opponents and superior officers, how cleverly he pushed his partners around, and what exceptional influence he had at very high levels.

He was simply incapable of listening. His one desire was to command. I found it impossible to go into anything thoroughly with him. He darted from one subject to another. He had no time for discussion or reflection. He made his decisions without due consideration. He rarely conceded any point. It was quite out of the question to get him to change his mind.

Owing to the many tasks he undertook, he was on the go day and night and spread nothing but unrest, hurry, and nervousness around him. His ambition, lust for power, mistrust, and vengefulness were matched only by his morbid inferiority complex and his mimosa-like sensitivity. With all this, he was well aware of his limitations. Anyone who had the advantage of him in education, experience, knowledge, or ability was not suffered anywhere near him on equal terms. He surrounded himself with youthful followers who could be dazzled by his zest and tireless energy, and with weak creatures who applauded his caprices and his brutal jests, feared him, flattered his vanity, and believed him to be the great coming man. He was far too shrewd, however, not to be able to see through such people. He played with their destinies like a mischievous child with tin soldiers. He was cunningly deferential and amiable to his superiors; arrogant, brutal, overbearing, intolerably haughty to those below him. He had no moral inhibitions whatever in getting what he wanted.

At the time I was still only an interested spectator. I watched the man as one watches a rare and ferocious beast of prey in a cage. His powers were limited to the control of building needed for production under Degenkolb, and I did not suspect that he had seen in our undertaking the great opportunity of his life. He did not yet seem dangerous to me; I was soon to know better.

CHAPTER 21

HIMMLER STRIKES AGAIN

At the beginning of January 1944 we had a great setback in developing A-4. It was found that some of the rockets exploded during the early part of the flight when the motor was still working, while others exploded or broke up in the air near the end of the trajectory, before impact. We sought the cause of the trouble but our efforts were impeded by the beginnings of production, which we had awaited so long. We were unable to fire experimental series with large numbers of rockets. It was impossible to proceed a step at a time. To respond to the pressure from above for a speed-up in production for active service we had to try several modifications at a time on each one of our few precious missiles. We could never hope to get a clear picture by such methods.

By the beginning of March we had some idea of the reasons for the explosions occurring during burning, but the cause of the airbursts at the end of the trajectory was still unknown.

In the early hours of March 15, 1944, a cold winter's night, the bedside telephone rang in my quarters at Schwedt on the Oder. I found myself talking to General of the Infantry Buhle, chief of the Army Staff serving the Armed Forces High Command at the Führer's headquarters in Berchtesgaden. I was to come immediately for a conference with Field Marshal Keitel. Accommodations had been reserved for me in the Berchtesgadener Hof.

I left Schwedt at 8 o'clock in the morning with my driver in my Opel Admiral, joined the main road at Joachimsthal and drove by way of Berlin, Hof, and Munich to Berchtesgaden. We were delayed by snowstorms, icy roads, and the havoc of a heavy air raid on Munich the night before, so that it was not until late afternoon that I reached Berchtesgaden. I rang up Buhle. He had been expecting me and would come over at once. He wished to speak to me in my room.

A quarter of an hour later he was telling me, "This morning at eight o'clock Professor von Braun and the two engineers Klaus Riedel and Gröttrup were arrested for sabotage of the A-4 project and taken to Stettin."

I could not believe my ears. That couldn't possibly be true! Von Braun, my best man, with whom I had worked in the closest collaboration for over ten years and whom I believed I knew better than anyone, whose whole soul and energy, whose indefatigable toil by day and by night, were devoted to the A-4, arrested for sabotage! It was incredible. And Klaus Riedel, who had worked out the entire ground organization with untiring zeal and absolutely outstanding perception of military needs, who was one of our most devoted followers! And Gröttrup, too, Dr. Steinhoff's deputy! Sheer insanity!

I asked, "What are they accused of?"

"You'll be told that tomorrow by the Field Marshal himself."

After a practically sleepless night I called on Keitel next morning at 9 o'clock. The Field Marshal received me immediately in his office.

"You have heard that von Braun, Riedel, and another of your men were arrested early yesterday morning by the Gestapo?"

I nodded without speaking. He continued, "The charges were so serious that arrest was bound to follow. The men are likely to lose their lives. How people in their position can indulge in such talk passes my understanding."

I replied instantly, "Sir, I do not know what the individual charges are. But I vouch for von Braun and Riedel. Gröttrup I don't know so well. In his case I should have to hear what he is accused of."

Keitel looked astonished. "You would vouch for these men with your own life? You've made up your mind very quickly!"

"It surely goes without saying, sir, that I stand by my closest colleagues without hesitation or reservation."

Keitel said gravely, "Do you know that your 'closest colleagues' have stated in company at Zinnowitz that it had never been their intention to make a weapon of war out of the rocket? That they had worked, under pressure from yourself, at the whole business of development only in order to obtain money for their experiments and the confirmation of their theories? That their object all along has been space travel?"

So that was it! "Nevertheless, I still vouch for them. I have often said myself in introducing a demonstration at Peenemünde that our work on the A-4 is only the first tentative step into a new age of technology, that of the rocket. How often have I insisted that the time is now ripe for this turning point in human history! We have shown the way to space travel. We have provided proof of its possibility. If my men have committed sabotage by repeating such phrases I ought to be arrested too."

"The sabotage," Keitel explained, "is seen in the fact that these men have been giving all their innermost thoughts to space travel and consequently have not applied their whole energy and ability to production of the A-4 as a weapon of war."

I could only shake my head. "Who was the informer, sir? There can be nothing but malice behind this. Or does it come from someone without the first idea of what's involved?"

Keitel shrugged his shoulders. "I don't know. I know only what I have told you."

"These arrests will be ruinous for the whole project—especially as the rocket is soon due to come into service and we haven't even tracked down the latest trouble. There must be some incomprehensible misunderstanding or mistake."

Keitel again shrugged his shoulders. "I can't do anything about it. Himmler has taken over himself."

"Sir, all service and civilian staff at Peenemünde come under military law. Peenemünde is subject to military jurisdiction. The men must be taken out of the Gestapo's hands at once and transferred to military detention."

"I can't interfere now in the middle of the investigation but I will detail an observer from Counterintelligence to be present at the hearings. He will report direct to me. You think these men will be a vital loss, do you?"

"Sir, I wish to put on record that if these arrests stand, completion of development will be problematical and employment of the rocket in the field will have to be postponed indefinitely."

"You really think the consequences will be as serious as that?"

"At this stage von Braun and Riedel are the most important men in the program. Gröttrup, too, is indispensable to the electrical side as permanent representative of the head of the department. It is my duty to demand immediate release of these men in the interests of the program."

"Be reasonable! I can't release them without Himmler's agreement. I must also avoid the least suspicion of being less zealous than the Gestapo and Himmler in these things. You know my position here. I am watched. All my actions are noted. People are only waiting for me to make a mistake. If I ever have to go, the Officers' Corps will have lost the last intermediary between itself and the Führer, its last chance of exercising any influence at all. Then the only rulers will be the SS—and Himmler."

"Sir, may I go and see Himmler? It is my duty to give him my views and ask for the release of these gentlemen."

"I'll ring him up."

Keitel telephoned Himmler's adjutant and, giving the reason for the call, asked whether I could have an interview. We waited a few moments. Then came the answer.

Himmler refused to see me. He said I must apply to the SS Security office in Berlin and ask for SS General Kaltenbrunner.

Keitel asked me to treat what he had said in the strictest confidence. Then he dismissed me. I drove back to Schwedt in a white heat of rage.

The next morning at 11 o'clock, accompanied by my Chief of Staff, Lieutenant Colonel Thom, I called at the SS Security head office in Prinz Albrecht Strasse, Berlin. This palatial building, with its gigantic staircase, was already pretty battered by bombs. Plaster had come off roof and walls, windows had been shattered, and door panels wrenched away. Heavier damage had been boarded up. It was uncomfortably cold everywhere.

In Kaltenbrunner's absence we were received by SS General Müller. He was the unobtrusive type of police official who leaves no personal impression in the memory. Later all I could remember was a pair of piercing gray-blue eyes, fixed on me with an unwavering scrutiny. My first impression was one of cold curiosity and extreme reserve.

After sitting down with his back to the window he opened the conversation. "So you are General Dornberger? I've heard—and read—a great deal about you. I take it you've come to talk about the Peenemünde business."

"Yes. I ask for the immediate release of the gentlemen so surprisingly arrested by the SD.[1] In support of my request I should like to specify—"

He interrupted me. "I beg your pardon! In the first place, the gentlemen have not been arrested but are being held in protective custody for questioning by the police commissioner at Stettin. Second, the SD has absolutely nothing to do with it. As a general on the active list you should surely know, by 1944, the difference between the SD and the Gestapo."

"General, I have never in my life come into close contact with either, so don't know the subtle difference. As far as I am concerned, the Gestapo, the SD, and the police are all very much the same. An arrest, or, as you call it, holding in protective custody, is the same with all of them."

He gulped in somewhat angry fashion, but then asked me to go on. I told him in detail what work the arrested men had done and had still to do, and why they must be released at once if the whole project was not to be wrecked. Finally I gave him my own explanation of the alleged statements. He listened quietly, watching me with his unwavering stare.

He declined to commit himself until after the first investigation and claimed he had no documents at all. He promised to brief

[1] The SD, standing for *Sicherheits Dienst*, was a special subsection of Himmler's police organization.

Kaltenbrunner and speed the matter up. I asked him to put urgent pressure on Stettin and he promised to do so. Then I asked him for permission to visit the arrested men at Stettin. He gave it.

Suddenly he observed, "You are a very interesting case, General. Do you know what a fat file of evidence we have against you here?"

I shook my head in surprise. He raised his hand a few inches above the table. I couldn't help asking him, "Why don't you arrest me, then?"

"Because it would be pointless as yet. You are still regarded as our greatest rocket expert and we can't very well ask you to give expert evidence against yourself."

"Very good of you. But I really should like to know what all these things are that you have against me."

"Well, first of all there's the delay in the development of the A-4 missile. That's a question that will certainly have to be tackled one day."

"I entirely agree. But a lot of people are going to get a surprise when they see who's to blame. Anything else?"

"Yes. Your entire activities with rockets in the Army Weapons Department will have to be gone into."

"Ah, yes! Putting the brake on development, eh? Is that all? If so, it's damned little!"

"No. Those were only a few general points. Perhaps you would like to hear about a specific case at Peenemünde? The charge there is one of deliberate or culpably negligent incitement to sabotage."

"That's a rather serious charge. What was the occasion?"

"At the end of March last year you said at a meeting of your directors that the Führer had dreamed that the A-4 would never get to England. You said you were powerless against the Führer's dreams. By that expression you exercised a harmful, pessimistic, almost defeatist influence on the zeal and enthusiasm of your senior staff and so sabotaged rapid progress."

"I don't know who your authority is for what was said at the meeting, but if what really happened is of any interest to you, I'll be glad to give you an account."

"Please do."

"In March 1943, the Führer said in reply to one of Speer's repeated requests for higher priority for the A-4 program, 'I have dreamed that the rocket will never be operational against England. I can rely on my inspirations. It is therefore pointless to give more support to the project.' I personally saw, in Major General Hartmann's office at the Ministry of Munitions, a memorandum of this statement of the Führer's, printed in the large type characteristic of headquarters. Speer and Saur confirmed it. I then went to Peenemünde and called my directors together. I reminded them of the enormous difficulties we had overcome in the past and explained that the last obstacle to recognition consisted only of the Führer's dream. I said I must ask them to use their last ounce of energy to overcome this obstacle as well; the way to do it was to succeed in our experiments. It was then that I ordered the running film to be made of the tests on October 3, 1942, which as you know won the Führer's recognition for our project at the beginning of July 1943. I am convinced that it was this action of mine that spurred and inspired my colleagues to a supreme effort in the face of a crushing blow. However, if it looks like sabotage to you, put me in the dock."

Müller said nothing.

I continued, "I don't know what you'd call this interview, with its suggestion of big criminal proceedings hanging over me. Do you imagine it will make me particularly happy in my work?"

With that, I left him. I went to Stettin and a few days later, working closely with Major Klammroth, who handled our affairs in the Counterintelligence Department of the High Command, managed to get von Braun transferred to Schwedt and then released altogether. I called for him at night, at Stettin, armed with a big bottle of brandy.

Soon afterward I was also able to welcome Riedel and Gröttrup back to my office. My declaration on oath that the arrested men were indispensable to the program had freed them provisionally for three months. At the end of this time another declaration to the same effect brought a similar adjournment. Then came the revolt of July 20, 1944, soon afterward the V-2 was put into operation, and the case lapsed.

I learned later that the arrests were the result of reports received from spies placed by Himmler's organization among the people of Zinnowitz after his first visit to Peenemünde. Apparently the spies had concentrated on us rather than on local inhabitants and strangers, and by taking words out of their context had twisted them to appear treasonable.

CHAPTER 22

DR. KAMMLER, SPECIAL COMMISSIONER

From November 1943, Dr. Kammler frequently attended our test and practice shots. He took part in conferences as Himmler's representative and came to the firing practice without being asked. He talked to individuals, listened to opinions and differences of opinion, insinuated himself into the confidence of the too trusting. Finally he took a hand in the game himself and started playing one man off against another. Gradually he collected the trump cards.

I saw the danger.

On May 31, 1944, I sent in a memorandum through Colonel General Fromm, once again requesting that I be given unequivocal authority over the whole project, from research to field operations. I ended by openly threatening to apply directly to the supreme authority. The situation left me no alternative. If the Army were not to lose control completely my terms would have to be met.

Fromm summoned me. I was reprimanded, threatened with punishment, my honor was impugned by a charge of unsoldierly conduct and cowardly dereliction of duty, all with the objective of inducing me to modify my demands. I did not yield. Fromm again confirmed the long-recognized powers I already held under his own jurisdiction. He said he would apply to Hitler for their extension.

I don't know whether he really did so. I was left dangling in midair and got no decision.

What I had feared now happened. In the middle of July, Himmler wrote to Field Marshal Keitel. He demanded the subordination of the various commissioners and departments to a single strong personality. He called for the appointment of a Commissioner General. Kammler believed he had won the game.

I drafted a reply for Keitel to send to Himmler, to the effect that the branches still outside my control ought now at long last to be subordinated to me, as I had proposed on May 31. However, the reply which Keitel actually sent was of a different nature. It was diplomatic and noncommittal. Keitel wrote that he believed the present organization would bring success. The decisive factor in the formulation of this letter was the attitude of the Army Weapons Department, which was opposed to the appointment of a Commissioner General, believing that such an appointment would lessen its own influence.

The department had taken steps to guard against the imminent danger. On June 1, 1944, the development works proper of the Peenemünde Army Establishment had been made a private concern under a managing director who had been borrowed from Siemens and was practically a stranger to our work. The difficulties were tolerated because the measure would prevent the seizure of Peenemünde by any military or semimilitary organization. The danger now came from another direction. The interest taken by industry and the Technological Office of the Party had ceased after the air raid. From a military point of view an entirely new organization was being built up.

Kammler took the position that since Colonel Zanssen was unacceptable to the SS, he could not act as my representative at conferences and tests at the SS practice ground at Heidelager, where, at Hitler's orders, practice firings had been carried out since November 1943. As I have mentioned before, the Army Weapons Department by this time had grown tired of the struggle and Zanssen was dropped.

Zanssen's successor, Major General Rossmann, did not feel able to take over all his duties. My old department, called *Wa Prüf 11* (Weapon Test 11), which had covered the whole field of Army rocket development—that is, both Peenemünde and Experimental Station Kummersdorf West—was split up. Weapon Test 11 was now to be concerned only with powder-rocket development.

Under General Rossmann a new development section for liquid-propellant rockets, Weapon Test 10, was called into being at Peenemünde.

For the time being I was powerless. An order, dated September 1943, by Colonel General Fromm, Director of Armaments and Commander-in-Chief of the Home Front, had made me directly responsible to him as his commissioner for the A-4 program. My sphere of duty extended from development to the formation and final training of field units for operations. In this way I parted from the Army Weapons Department, to which I had belonged for 17 years, but kept my influence on development.

By another order, also signed by Fromm, at the end of December 1943, the Army Weapons Department had tried to recover control of the Peenemünde establishment. I had protested, for despite my position as commissioner for the whole program I had been bypassed in the drafting of the order. The situation was by no means clear. The Army Weapons Department feared that my appointment as commissioner would undermine its hitherto dominating position in weapon development in the Army. The department would have preferred to see me restricted to the formation and training of operational field units.

After Fromm's unsatisfactory decision on my request for full powers on May 31, 1944, my influence on development was curtailed. Questions of organization and administration at Peenemünde were decided by the Army Weapons Department alone.

A hopeless muddle was the result.

I saw the trouble coming. When the fresh reorganization took place in July 1944, I openly and emphatically denounced the measures as a crime at such a time, critical as it was both politically and by reason of the failures at Heidelager. I was sent for, reproved, and reprimanded. Change the situation I could not.

Kammler's stay at Heidelager had given him some insight into our domestic disputes. He went on collecting material. For some months he had been labeling Professor von Braun as too young, too childish, too supercilious and arrogant for his job. Degenkolb he represented merely as a hopeless alcoholic.

There remained myself. On July 8, 1944, I was described by Kammler, in the presence of General Buhle and two other generals, as a public danger. He said I ought to be court-martialed. He said that for years I had been weakening Germany's armament potential by tying enormous armament capacity both in men and material to a more than questionable attempt to bring a chimera into existence. It would be a crime to devote another penny to so hopeless a project.

Kammler had put his cards on the table. On July 20, 1944, after the attempt on Hitler's life, Himmler took over Fromm's department. By August 4 Kammler, now a SS lieutenant general, had been given provisional supervision of the A-4 program. On August 8 Himmler appointed him his special commissioner for the entire program, with full powers, over his own signature: ". . . acts on my orders and his directions and instructions are to be obeyed." The order was definite and beyond all doubt. It was what I had been fighting for years to obtain for myself.

Thus, after nearly all the obstacles to tactical employment of the A-4 had been overcome, an uninformed layman took the leadership: a man who only a month before had clearly professed his disbelief in the project by describing it as a chimera without prospect of realization and its continued development as a crime against the German people.

The struggle for control of the new weapon was apparently over. A month later the V-2 was put into military operation.

CHAPTER 23

ELEVENTH-HOUR STRUGGLES

"Look at this, Doctor! Don't you think it might be a clue?"

"I think not. The charred layer is hardly a millimeter thick. The strength of the wood has not been affected."

I held in my hand a small piece of wood charred on one side. The frictional heating to nearly 1260 degrees Fahrenheit on return of the missile to the earth's atmosphere in the course of braking had charred the surface of an aerial frame, made of wood because of its insulating properties. The area of wood over which the supporting piece of sheet metal had been nailed was unaffected.

We were standing with the chief of the target observation squad, First Lieutenant Ruckteschel, in a small shed in a village in the middle of Poland. All round us, spread out on the ground, lay pieces of aluminum from torn tanks, smashed fins, and fragments of pumps and rocket motors. In one corner was piled a heap of twisted pieces of the outer skin, broken electrical relays, tangles of conductor wires, gyroscopes, and rudder machinery. Among them lay the egg-shaped tanks for hydrogen peroxide, and sections of aluminum pipe.

We had flown once again in the Storch to the target area to see whether we could identify in the assembled wreckage of the A-4 the source of our failures and troubles of the last few months. Hitherto we had been groping in the dark. We could not find the source. We could only guess.

Since the end of November 1943 practically all our test shots had been carried out in Poland. Until August 1943 we had always fired over the sea from Peenemünde. Two of our rockets had gone wild. They had fallen in the wooded country west and north of Gdynia. Fortunately they had neither injured people nor damaged buildings. The craters were up to 100 feet across and over 30 feet deep. They had produced only very small iron splinters under half an inch in length. These were dark blue and quite unidentifiable. It had been obvious beyond doubt in these cases that the entire missile had fallen.

The warheads of the rockets had not contained high explosive. To produce operational flying conditions we had filled the warheads with sand. The live detonator had also been replaced by a dummy.

The color bags carried on rockets launched out to sea had ensured that in practically all cases the point of impact could be spotted by the reconnaissance plane from the bright green stains on the water, and the range and dimensions measured. We were of the firm opinion that the end of the trajectory left nothing to be desired.

After the air raid of August 17 on Peenemünde the question arose whether we should go on firing from there. At the beginning of September an order came from headquarters to shoot overland with the newly formed experimental battery 444 from Heidelager at Blizna in Poland. Overland firing across very great distances had been practiced before, from one firing range across thinly populated districts to another, in the course of experiments with long-range artillery.

I obtained a ruling from the legal department of the Army High Command on the responsibility incurred if stray rockets caused injury to the civilian population. The opinion was that the firing organization could not be held responsible if all reasonable precautions had been taken. Responsibility would have to be borne by the department which had issued the orders to shoot and had approved the direction and target area.

I reported this ruling to the Führer's headquarters through Service channels. A few days later I received an order from headquarters: "Approval of the target area will be given by the Reichsführer SS [Himmler]. The military commander of the region must be notified. The Army firing party is responsible only for the safety of the area immediately surrounding the firing point. Outside that area the Reichsführer SS bears full responsibility for all accidents."

In this way the Blizna firing range in the great forests of the Vistula-San triangle came into being. In the thick woods of fir, pine, and oak there was a big clearing measuring a little over half a square mile. A small, stone-built house and a dilapidated thatched stable stood there in complete isolation. During October and November barracks, living quarters, portable vehicle shelters, and a large magazine were erected close by.

A railroad track running up to the barracks and between the sheds connected us with the Cracow-Lemberg line. A concrete road built in a few weeks led from the nearest main highway to our testing ground far from all human habitation. A double barbed-wire fence enclosed the area.

Immediately after the air raid on Peenemünde I had established a training school for long-range rocket troops under Colonel Stegmeier at Köslin on the Baltic, to prepare specialists for active service. The school had a teaching staff, an experimental staff, and an experimental battery, the 444. At the end of October this battery and the experimental staff under Major Weber were transferred to Blizna. Target areas had been approved by the Reichsführer SS.

From the very start Heidelager had bad luck. When, on November 5, 1943, with the temperature nearly 14 degrees Fahrenheit, the first practice rounds were fired there, I had been detained in Berlin by some conference. One of the many tasks of this experiment was to decide what type of ground would be needed for a smooth firing. The experimental battery had so far fired only a few rockets and was still inexperienced. At the first test at Blizna it was assumed that loose sand, the surface frozen over to a depth of only half an inch, would be adequate as a base. Owing to some unfortunate carelessness, the blast-deflector plate of the firing table was not set firmly on the ground at ignition time. The gas jet thawed out the ground and burrowed down into the sand.

One leg of the firing table sank slowly into the soil during the preliminary stage. The rocket rose at a slant, went out of control, and crashed into the forest 2 miles away.

That would not have been so bad if General Heinemann, commanding the field employment of V-weapons, had not been watching a rocket shot for the first time. From this false start, due entirely to the inexperience of the man in charge, the conclusion was drawn that only firm concrete platforms would serve for front-line operations. For over 6 months manpower and material were wasted on the erection of these concrete emplacements in the battle area. Even after we had successfully fired from lumber-reinforced forest soil, somewhat prepared and even unprepared natural forest paths, this still went on. The first impression stuck, and nobody could do anything about it.

Troubles now came thick and fast. Shot after shot went wrong and confronted us with apparently insoluble problems.

There were three types of failures. Some rockets rose barely 60 feet. Vibration of some sort would cause a relay contact to break, burning would stop, and the missile would fall back to earth and explode. Firing tables and cable sets, of which only a few were available, were destroyed by such premature Brennschluss. It was difficult to replace the lost accessories and an unreasonably long time went by before the next round.

Other rockets made a good start but then unaccountably exploded at 3000 to 6000 feet or even higher. The rocket was destroyed and with it all evidence of the cause.

Others, again, made a perfect flight, but over the target area a white cloud of steam suddenly appeared in the sky, a short, sharp, double report rang out, the warhead crashed, and a shower of wreckage fell to earth. The rocket, after covering 160 miles, had unaccountably blown up at a height of a few thousand feet. Only 10 to 20 per cent of the rockets launched reached their target without a hitch. I was in despair. Could Dr. Thiel and the senior staff at Peenemünde have been right after all? Was our flying laboratory too much for soldiers to handle? Had we really been overconfident? Was it a hopeless business?

Engineers and technicians from Peenemünde joined the experimental battery. It made no difference.

Could the troubles be due to faulty production at the Mittelwerk? Our predictions on the rate of production had been promptly confirmed. The first rockets were all too slow in emerging from the exit tunnel of the underground factory. For our practice rounds we took our rockets wherever we could get them: from Peenemünde, where we had assembled them ourselves, or from the Mittelwerk's experimental output. We had the same failures with all of them.

There were conferences, journeys, and more conferences. Experts from Peenemünde were placed in the assembly works and the factories producing subassemblies. All components were tested over and over again without yielding a clue. We were getting too few rockets to use a systematic method in our researches, and whether we hit on the solution was a matter of chance.

Top-level brass was pressing hard; we had to work fast. Visitors from headquarters drove away with long faces. I felt too desperate myself to be able to reassure them.

On top of this came difficulties with the field formations. These troops, now that they had theoretical knowledge, had to be trained in firing practice. In the end we had three batteries at Heidelager simultaneously, along with the engineer groups. We consoled ourselves with the reflection that the main thing for the troops was to be able to service the rocket correctly and launch it with speed and precision. Here they could very easily learn this.

Many of the soldiers had been craftsmen and engineers in civilian life. They were keen, and interested in the technical aspects. They got on very well with the Peenemünde engineers. A steady stream of practical suggestions for improvement flowed into the development works. As a result of shooting in all kinds of weather and the most varied field conditions the skill of the crews rose to a degree of perfection that had not been reached even on the testing ground at Peenemünde. The fears of my colleagues had proved groundless.

The behavior of the rocket in flight, however, was entirely Peenemünde's responsibility, and it was up to our technicians, in association with the experimental staff, to find out what was wrong.

In the middle of this period, the most unfortunate in the whole history of the rocket, came the changes in organization decreed by the Army Weapons Department. Zanssen was dismissed, my old department was split up, Peenemünde was transformed into a private concern, and the new departments set up under General Rossmann. The months went by, but meanwhile firing practice had to go on and sources of error had to be traced.

In addition to the somewhat shaky powers I possessed I had one decided advantage, which I was firmly resolved to exploit. At Heidelager no rocket was fired except by soldiers under my command. Nearly all practice shots by the development works and by the newly created development section for liquid-propellant rockets had to take place in Heidelager. I therefore held the reins.

In the end things settled down. When it came to finding ways and means of rescuing the project from complete ruin, everyone helped. At the long table in the mess the officers and engineers of the field units conferred in friendly harmony with General Rossmann and the directors of the development works, the production managers newly arrived by plane, and the available technicians. But we were not out of the woods yet.

After a tedious investigation which followed up all existing clues and all possibilities, we succeeded in almost eliminating explosions during the ascending portion of the trajectory. The curved fuel-distribution pipes had often been tensed in assembly. The shock of ignition of the rocket motor and the vibrations occurring while it burned had sometimes loosened the fittings of the fuel pipes at both ends. The result was that a droplet mist of alcohol had been sprayed into the stern section of the rocket, had formed an explosive mixture with the air present, and been ignited by the exhaust flame. Extra locking devices on the fittings and improvement of the pipe-bending machinery to insure a tension-free fit prevented a repetition of this particular trouble. The reasons for the failure of the relay contact, which had given us such terrible headaches, seemed to have been discovered. Yet we were still unable to bring more than 30 per cent of the rockets down to earth with a normal impact.

Once more we carefully examined the various fragments of the wreckage. The heating of the thin outer skin did not seem to weaken the strength of the construction. Only the paint on the outside of the skin of the rocket had been burned away or blistered. The protective coat on the inside of the 0.025-inch-thick metal skin showed no traces whatever of excessive heat. Examination of the sheet metal by the Peenemünde materials research section disclosed nothing to cause anxiety. Nevertheless, the explosions continued.

It was clear that despite everything heat must somehow be responsible for the explosions. Either the alcohol tank burst, perhaps because the temperature of 896 degrees Fahrenheit, with the valves closed, caused the alcohol and air mixture in the fuel tank to explode, or else it was the oxygen tank that exploded. It could not be the hydrogen peroxide of the turbine drive, for those tanks were only dented, not burst.

We discussed the whole question over and over again. Von Braun declared that the alcohol tank and its ventilation were the culprit. I was more inclined to blame the oxygen tank. After Brennschluss the tanks still contained anywhere up to 1000 pounds of liquids, depending on mixture ratio and burning time. To support his view von Braun explained to me for the hundredth time the ventilation system of the alcohol tank. At all costs we had to prevent the practically empty tank from exploding through overheating or being torn open by the increased air pressure when the rocket re-entered the earth's atmosphere. If the latter happened the fuel would get into the body of the rocket. The graphite vanes would still be red-hot, as there is only slight loss of heat by radiation in airless space, and they could easily ignite drops of fuel sucked out of the stern by the slipstream. For this reason we had made sure that throughout the trajectory pressure in the tank never fell below 20.5 pounds per square inch. For the first 40 seconds of ascent we utilized the ram pressure of the air, which was able to enter the tank through a tube from the warhead.

After that, however, the air became too thin to maintain the tank pressure, and a valve automatically shut it off and switched over to a high-pressure nitrogen flask carried in the rocket. Von Braun thought that failure of this complicated mechanism might well be the trouble.

We then checked again on the connections between the four main sections of the rocket—the warhead, the instrument compartment, the central section containing the tanks, and the stern holding the motor. The great steel rings, the bulkheads between the main hull components, were secured by screws. The bulkheads were bent, to be sure, but they were undamaged. The screws had held.

Nevertheless, just behind the top bulkhead the skin had been torn away. Was that by any chance a weak spot? So far tests and calculations said no.

Suppose it were the oxygen tank after all? Heating of the oxygen, which evaporates at minus 186 degrees centigrade, might suddenly increase pressure and explode the tank. We had no proof. We knew nothing about it. In earlier test shots at Peenemünde the figures received from the rocket by our telemetering system during flight had been inconclusive.

We had systematically replaced all aluminum parts of the outer skin, such as rivets and door latches of the instrument compartment, by steel ones. The entire structure was checked again and again. The wind-tunnel figures were verified. These showed that the rocket should stand all stresses which might conceivably be imposed on it. The puzzle remained unsolved.

I asked von Braun whether it was possible that the rocket disintegrated first and exploded afterward. I could imagine parts of the skin of the instrument compartment, or those immediately behind the bulkhead in the forward third of the center section, perhaps working loose under the increased stress of the second passage through the atmosphere, and being torn away as their stability was weakened by heat. The rocket might become unstable through the ram pressure exerted through the opening, the tanks might tear open, and explosion would naturally follow. Von

Braun considered this out of the question. We came to no conclusion.

An hour afterward we were in a small observation trench at the foot of a long, low hill. All round us the slightly undulating Polish landscape stretched to infinity. No human habitation of any kind could be seen for miles. South of us, toward Blizna, a wide depression, barren except for a few scattered bushes and clumps of trees, lay athwart the line of fire. The winding curves of a clear little stream sparkled in the sunshine.

We were exactly at the spot marked on the map as the current target area. That morning the first rocket had come down successfully 150 yards away on the slope. It had dug a formidable hole, and reddish-brown lumps of clay, almost as big as a man, lay scattered far and wide in the fields of green rye round the crater.

We had never yet been able to catch with our binoculars the white cloud heralding an explosion at the moment of its appearance. The vault of a cloudless blue sky enclosed the shimmering, sunlit air.

Our radio reported that the rocket had been launched. We set our stopwatches. Flying time from Blizna to our observation post would be 5 minutes, 13 seconds.

We discussed our troubles as we waited, watching the minute hand. After 5 minutes I took my binoculars and looked aloft in the direction from which the rocket would be coming. I searched the sky slowly. Suddenly, in a fraction of a second, I saw a tiny dot that lengthened into a short streak. Almost at the same instant a white cloud of steam formed, brilliantly lit by the sun. I saw one part of the rocket flying on and recognized the warhead and instrument compartment. As the sharp double report abruptly broke a silence that had been complete except for the trilling of larks, I saw the dust thrown up by the impact about 2000 yards ahead of us and large parts of the rocket falling slowly to the ground. I had seen the beginning of an airburst through my field glasses.

Had the idea that had been in my mind for some time given me an illusion of something which could hardly be visible at a speed of nearly 2000 miles per hour? I had had the impression that before the explosion cloud appeared, the rocket, deflected from its course, had stood at an angle of nearly 20 degrees to the trajectory, broken up into two parts, and only then exploded. Had that slant-wise position been merely an optical illusion? Or was this the beginning of the airburst?

I could not swear to what I had seen. The whole thing had been too quick. Von Braun had not seen the white cloud—which in my opinion was nothing but the oxygen residue suddenly evaporating in the air after the break-up of the rocket—until well after it was formed.

We examined the wreckage at the point of impact, but it gave us no fresh information. We then flew back to Blizna to discuss with General Rossmann and the senior Peenemünde staff members what was to be done. After a long debate we decided to carry out von Braun's proposal: fire five test rounds in which the rocket would be made to burn the alcohol tank completely dry. If no alcohol were present at the end of trajectory, then obviously it could not be the cause of the trouble.

We also adopted a proposal by General Rossmann that the alcohol and oxygen tanks in six rockets should be insulated with glass wool against transfer of heat from the outer skin. The chief designer from Peenemünde, the third of the three unrelated Riedels, did not believe in this expedient. In his view the air between the outer skin and the tanks had an effect similar to that of the vacuum in a vacuum flask; therefore transfer of heat could not be responsible.

We further decided to step up the Peenemünde test firings which had gradually been starting up again. Mostly we would fire vertically from the Greifswalder Oie, and the rocket, falling a few miles from the island, would be photographed throughout its flight by cinetheodolites and phototheodolites, and if possible by slow-motion camera. We hoped that the photographs would tell us whether it was a structural fault, aerodynamic instability, or some other cause that was to blame for the airbursts. The rockets would also be fitted with the new data transmitters, a telemetering system with twenty-four channels of information, which would reveal danger points while the rocket was in flight.

The rockets adjusted to burn the last drop of alcohol in their fuel tanks produced the customary percentage of airbursts. Therefore the alcohol tank was evidently not responsible.

When I returned to Heidelager a few days later three rockets with glass-wool insulation had already been fired that morning. All made their impacts. That afternoon we achieved three further impacts. The problem which had held us up for months seemed to be solved. Whether this was due to the prevention of heat transfer from the outer skin to the tanks, or to a stiffening of the center section by the glass wool, or to greater stability as a result of the shift in the center of gravity, the fact remained that for the first time six successive rounds had produced six impacts. We were filled with hope and thought ourselves justified at last in devoting time to increasing the effect of the individual rocket.

The sheer momentum of a rocket weighing over 4.5 tons and traveling at 1500 miles per hour caused a crater 30 to 40 yards wide and 10 to 15 yards deep even without an explosive charge. Apart from fairly violent earth tremors, no lateral effects were produced beyond the edge of the crater.

The warhead of 1/4-inch steel was originally designed to hold an explosive charge of 1 metric ton. To lessen deadweight our first plans for the A-4 were based entirely on the use of aluminum and magnesium alloys. Calculations based on wind-tunnel experiments showed that the temperature of the skin would reach 1250 degrees Fahrenheit, and orders to avoid these alloys, which were scarce, compelled us to substitute sheet steel. Deadweight was thus increased. To get anywhere near the required range of 160 miles, we had to give up the idea of carrying 1 ton of explosive and restrict to that figure the total weight of the warhead including the steel casing. The problem now was to explode the warhead at the right height above the target, to get the maximum lateral effect from the momentum of the projectile. My intention was to fit a proximity fuze that could explode the warhead about 60 feet above the target, but it proved impossible, throughout the war, to get such a device manufactured in Germany. We had to be content with detonation on impact.

The fuze would have to be electrical because with any mechanical fuze the interval between ignition and detonation was too great; in consequence of its high speed the rocket would shatter on impact long before the explosion. The fuze would also have to be sensitive enough to be actuated instantaneously at the lightest touch and the slightest shock, causing the charge to explode before the warhead penetrated too far into the ground.

Now that the impact problem appeared to have been solved we were at last in a position to experiment with a sensitive fuze of this type. As long as the rocket had been liable to break up in transit the resulting shock would have made the sensitive electrical fuze explode the warhead uselessly in the air.

To our great disappointment further experiments with rockets insulated by glass wool showed that our optimism had been premature. True, the figure of impacts increased to nearly 70 per cent, but 30 per cent still exploded in the air. By various means we at length succeeded in stepping up the hits to 80 per cent by the time the rocket went into action, but it was not until the closing months of the war that we found the final solution by reinforcing the front end of the hull with a sheet-steel collar that we riveted in place. In the end we achieved 100 per cent impacts.

In the summer of 1944, however, we faced the important question of whether to use a sensitive fuze, and accept a 30-per-cent wastage from airbursts, or a less sensitive fuze which would be impervious to the shock of disintegration in the air. In hundreds of cases we had found that the warhead and the adjoining instrument compartment flew on alone after disintegration of the rocket and reached the ground undamaged. If we used the less sensitive fuze, we could expect to achieve some effect even with the 30 per cent that broke up in the air.

Time pressed and the patience of the supreme authorities was at an end. We had no further choice. While we still hoped to put

an end to airburst altogether, we had nevertheless to bring ourselves to give the rocket a less sensitive fuze for operations at the
cost of reducing its effectiveness as a weapon.

All these questions kept us at high pitch throughout the first
half of 1944. Opinions clashed and nerves were stretched to breaking point. Production at the Mittelwerk had to be interrupted
every time a series of rockets was required for experiments on
suggested modifications. Until the modifications had been tested,
further production had to be postponed.

The supreme authorities of the Reich demanded mass production. *We* now had to strain every muscle to make up for *their*
neglect in past years. So it came about that many compromises
were perforce accepted, which could never be satisfactory to us
as the creators of this long-range rocket. They resulted in our
having to send to the front a missile far short of what it could have
been, a missile inadequate in accuracy and effect, which was
exactly what we had anxiously striven for years to avoid, a weapon
which, despite its technical merits, was unequal to its task.

CHAPTER 24

FLIGHT INTO SPACE

Practice shooting was going on at the Heidelager.

For weeks Battery 444 had been operating from an emplacement of wooden beams at a spot where the forest jutted out into the clearing. The bark had been stripped off the tall fir trees to a height of several yards by the searing gas jet. Charring on the trunks showed how many rockets had been fired. Glittering streaks of resin oozed over the mortal wounds of trees that were defending themselves against annihilation. The gloomy picture of destruction was completed by several huge craters made by rockets that had dropped back and exploded.

We stood on the low observation hill about 300 yards away from the small stone house and the dilapidated stable. The first projectile took off. The sun was behind us and its rays illuminated the rocket in its coat of dull-green camouflage paint, with its long glowing exhaust, as it rose vertically above the black woods. A great rumbling filled the air.

I watched closely through my binoculars, following the rocket's rapid acceleration. Ought it not to start curving now? It was only slightly tilted in the target direction. It rose higher and higher. Scattered white shreds of cloud hovered far up in the clear sky.

The rocket had hardly glided past the clouds when I saw something I had never noticed before showing up distinctly against the dark background. It was as though the projectile had suddenly had sugar icing poured over it. It shone brilliantly white in the dazzling sunlight. Moisture in the form of hoarfrost must have been deposited on it from a warm and humid layer of air after it had passed through a cooler layer. The phenomenon vanished as suddenly as it had appeared.

Then it was repeated higher up.

This rocket had risen at least 30 miles higher than its predecessors. How much valuable information it might have brought back to earth! Zigzags forming in vapor trails in a matter of seconds had already indicated differences in direction and velocity of the wind in successive air layers—something well worth further study.

To be borne upward like this almost into airless space—what a wonderful experience it would be for mankind! What a wealth of knowledge it could offer! I could imagine the eagerness with which meteorologists, physicists, and astronomers would look forward to their first voyage into the stratosphere and ionosphere. How slight, after all, is our knowledge of the outer covering of our small planet, based as it still is purely on conjecture and inference! We had often talked about the design and appearance of a space rocket: how windows giving an uninterrupted view from the spaceship could be made to keep off injurious ultraviolet rays from the sun; how, in the chill of cosmic space, a reasonable temperature might be maintained by means of black and white paint and the alternate turning toward the sun of heat-absorbing and heat-reflecting surfaces. How wonderful it would be to fly in unimaginable and utter silence, since even at a height of 40 miles the wide separation of air molecules makes the transmission of sound utterly impossible! With what enthusiasm the scientists of the world would attack the electrically charged layers that surround the earth; what a fantastic sight it would be when the colors of the earth, brilliantly lit by the sun, slowly dissolved beneath the rocket, and the spaceship, in broad daylight, rose into a sky gradually changing from violet to deepest black and spangled with stars of a glittering, metallic blue!

Long before the war we had looked upon our rocket as a possible means of investigating the upper atmosphere. We had got into touch with Professor Regener of Stuttgart, with the intention of having him carry on his work on high-altitude and cosmic radiation in conjunction with us. Army and Air Force meteorologists developed and manufactured recording instruments which could be recovered by parachute. These people were always asking us to be allowed to experiment with our missiles. We had to refuse. We needed every rocket for the purpose of overcoming our own technical difficulties. Employment at the front seemed more urgent to us in wartime than this research, important and interesting as it might be scientifically. I was firmly resolved to use our rocket for it after the war, but for the moment the rapid march of events left me little time for dreams of the future.

An hour later the battery launched its second rocket.

We had still been having occasional difficulties with the steering gear. Twice already a rocket had gone wild after rising a few yards and crashed somewhere close by in the woods. So far, however, the straying had not been in our direction.

I had visited the emplacement, watched the final preparations for launching, gone up on to the platform on the raised boom of the Meillerwagen, talked to the crew, and checked the adjustment of the reducing valve. I had noted with my stopwatch the time taken to tank up and get the rocket ready. Tanking-up time had dropped to 12 minutes.

At the edge of the forest was a small slit trench from which there was a good view of the rocket standing vertically on its firing table, which was set in a narrow path through the woods about 75 yards away. I intended to be in this trench so that I could follow once more every detail of the launching.

On my way there I discussed various recent ignition difficulties with a member of the experimental staff. Time seemed to stand still, as it always did just before take-off. While we were walking up and down between the emplacement and the observation hill the rocket had been made ready for launching. The fire order was given. I hadn't time to get to the trench.

When the main stage started, the rising rocket oscillated badly. The tail fins struck the overhanging branches of a pine. The instruments lost control and the rocket turned over at an angle of 90 degrees with its motor working at full thrust. Flying only just above the treetops, the rocket described a flattened arc and crashed at the very edge of the small trench. The tanks, still almost full, exploded in a gigantic flash of reddish-blue flame. Fragments of metal and equipment flew in all directions out of the enormous cloud of smoke and dust.

The trench had been occupied by men of the firing battery. Thus, before its actual employment on active service, the long-range rocket claimed its first victims from our own ranks. A few days later we buried four members of the experimental battery in the idyllic surroundings of a little forest cemetery.

Shortly afterward I spent some time at Peenemünde, attending conferences. As darkness was coming on and the first stars began to gleam in the evening sky, I was standing on the lofty concrete platform of Test Stand I, looking toward the Greifswalder Oie and waiting patiently. At last, nearly an hour after sunset, a bright, growing flame showed above the woods. I could not see the actual missile, only the long, glowing gas jet rising eerily, flickering like a will-o'-the-wisp, into the dark sky.

From the beach close by the monotonous murmur of the surf broke the profound stillness. The roar of the rocket's motor could not be heard at this distance.

The projectile might have been between 1 and 2 miles high when, in its vertical ascent, it suddenly left the earth's shadow and was dazzlingly illuminated by the sun, which, for us, had already set. It could now be seen in clear relief against the dark sky. Conditions were ideal for observation and we could follow every movement.

The rocket had been only half fueled. We were not interested in setting an altitude record. On this occasion our object was to note what happened when the projectile re-entered the earth's atmosphere. We had launched vertically without provision for automatic tilting. Higher and higher into the dark evening sky rose the shining missile. It looked almost white. The flame of the motor had already been extinguished for some minutes. The rocket must by now have reached a height of 30 or 40 miles.

I had not seen the slightest oscillation or deviation from course.

The telescope, locked against lateral twist, only needed to be moved vertically to enable me, even at this distance, to keep the rocket in view. I could clearly distinguish in that small, bright streak the characteristic pointed nose and broad fins.

The speed of the missile had diminished. It had now reached the summit of its ascent. For a fraction of a second it seemed to stand still in space. It was bound to tilt now and point its tip earthward, like any other stable body.

But no! Of course that could not happen. Up there neither air nor air resistance existed. There was no medium in which the tail fins could prove their stabilizing and steering properties. At that height the shape of a body made no difference. Only the center of gravity governed the line of flight. The rocket was bound to go on flying in the same position in which it had entered practically airless space.

I looked upward, holding my breath. Something which hitherto had been mere theory, something which so many visitors at our lectures and demonstrations had found so incomprehensible, inconceivable, I, with my own eyes, was now clearly witnessing for the first time.

The rocket fell vertically downward with its nose pointing up and the tail fins toward the ground. It was maintaining the position in which it had entered space.

The fall accelerated steadily. The missile grew bigger and bigger in the field of my telescope. Now! It must have reached the boundary of the earth's atmosphere. The whole thing happened in a matter of seconds, yet was clearly visible, so precise were the movements. The rocket described almost three-quarters of a revolution about its center of gravity. For one brief moment it seemed to lie diagonally across the direction of fall. Then the nose inclined earthward. After a few brief vibrations the missile, with its nose pointing vertically downward, fell with "arrow stability" for thousands of feet. Then it was once more swallowed up in the earth's shadow.

I had now witnessed, with convincing clarity, the phenomenon I had so often seen in the supersonic wind tunnel. So it was when the experimental engineer pressed the button and the air hissing through the orifice exerted pressure on the fin-stabilized model, forcing it to its stable position.

I could not see the impact on the water. Certainly there had been no disintegration in the air.

The experiment was repeated with data transmitters and full tanks. The take-offs went on day and night. Firing vertically, with 67 seconds of burning time, we achieved a height of 117.44 miles. Only once, however, did we succeed in getting a shot with the film camera of the moment at which the rocket broke up, and then no definite conclusion could be drawn from it. It was impossible to be sure whether the slightly diagonal position of the missile before it exploded in the air was the cause of disintegration or only its beginning.

CHAPTER 25

FOR AND AGAINST PEENEMÜNDE

To cause Brennschluss when the desired time interval after take-off had elapsed, we had so far used only the radio apparatus invented by Professor Wolman of Dresden. We measured the flight velocity by radio Doppler effect, and as soon as the speed required for a certain distance had been reached we switched off by radio. This procedure was susceptible to interference by suitable countermeasures. Moreover, the cost of installation was high and the demand for vacuum tubes heavy. There were ways, however, of protecting ourselves against Allied interference, whether premeditated or accidental, and this was an important function of the Department of Flight Instruments, Guidance, and Measurement. In the case of the beam-guidance method we experimented with development of centimeter-wave equipment. In the course of time all other radio devices were made proof against interference to a great extent. Also the rocket antennae were developed to act primarily in response to signals coming from the rear.

We were quite sure that the Allies would strain every nerve to disrupt the delicate working of our radio installations. It was a surprise to us in the field that there was not a single case of proved interference. We had prepared elaborate plans for radio security and also for interception and evaluation of information on activities, for everything depended upon our obtaining knowledge of countermeasures in good time.

While we were launching from Heidelager the first integrating accelerometers arrived. These were instruments intended to make us independent of radio and all the elaborate equipment hitherto in use. The new device, carried by the rocket in flight, was sensitive to acceleration, integrated the acceleration measured, and then indicated the speed of flight at the moment. It could be pre-set to switch off the fuel flow to the rocket motor as soon as the required speed was reached.

We carried out comparative tests. With the integrating acceler-ometer made by the Kreiselgeräte G.m.b.H., lateral dispersion was considerably worse than with the radio apparatus. With the equipment developed by Professors Buchhold and Wagner of Darmstadt it was about the same as with Professor Wolman's apparatus.

Although development of these inventions had begun in 1939, this was the first time we had been able to use them on our rockets. They were still not perfect. They measured only the velocity along the trajectory. We wished, however, to include in our calculations the distance covered by the rocket up to Brennschluss. For this the figures had to be integrated once more. Development of this double integrater was entrusted to Professor Buchhold but did not reach production stage while the war lasted.

Throughout our project we were always receiving from factories and technical institutes practical aid in simplifying our launching procedure. Up to the outbreak of war we had associated only a few firms with our work. We thought it necessary for security reasons to carry out most of the development ourselves. We made in our own works everything we thought we might not be able to get from industry. In addition, we improved equipment already in existence and adapted it for incorporation in the rocket.

The Peenemünde establishment and plant had been built on so great a scale that it would have been quite adequate for work in times of peace. When the war came development had to be speeded up, and the shortage of technicians compelled us to make widespread demands on technical institutes, laboratories, facto-ries, and other Service or government departments. With this we achieved first-rate results in practically all branches, and also, as a result of industry's taking over the manufacture of individual components, we received many stimulating suggestions for im-provement and development.

The question might now be asked: had we been correct in establishing our Peenemünde Army Experimental Station along the lines used? Ought we not, after all, to have tried to get industry to take over the development in its entirety, limiting our own activities to detailed requests and tests? Would it not have been better to put the whole thing on a broader basis at once and have several firms engaged in the work at the same time, as was usual in weapon development? Would it not have been better to make practical use of the truth that the more eyes there are, the more they see? Should we not, above all, have begun with the basic research and proceeded to practical research much later? Ought we not, rather, to have stimulated industry, subsidized it, and awaited results?

All well and good—but in that way we should never have reached the goal we set ourselves. If our task was successfully accomplished it was because of the work done at that early stage at Peenemünde, a stage in rocket development comparable only with that reached by air travel just after the First World War.

If we wanted results quickly we could not wait for basic research to be carried out. We did not, of course, deny its value. On the contrary, research can never be too comprehensive. From the beginning we had been aware of its vital importance. It was only basic research that could tell us "why," that could put us in possession of the elements of a problem. At the beginning of development a flood of contracts to carry out research found their way to scientists through the Research Branch of the Army Weapons Department. But we could not wait for their results. Because we were well aware that scientists cannot be forced to work to schedule we never tried to speed up this research work. We merely asked for reports when the work was completed. Thus much time went by.

Obviously development could not be held up for these long periods. As a first step we had to lay more stress on practical research and to combine it with development—to save time, among other reasons. Basic research had to run concurrently.

Hence the multiplicity of laboratories and installations in Peene-münde.

Then there was the question of money. We were well aware that the development of big, long-range rockets—missiles which, being fully automatic, would necessarily carry an infinite variety of the latest and most complex machinery modern technology could offer—would cost millions, nay, hundreds of millions of marks. Now, whether we allowed industry to proceed with development or undertook it ourselves would make very little difference to the cost. It would be impossible to dispense with any of the special plant, test fields, or test stands. Had we put several factories to work at the same time, the costs would only have increased. Individual components and instruments for installation in the rocket were, of course, another matter. Obviously these must be developed by industry.

Finally, we had to consider secrecy.

Looking back, I can say now that the way we chose was the right one. We had to create our own big research and development station for the long-range rocket. The question had been whether industry or the Armed Forces should take charge of development. In Germany in 1932 neither industry nor the Armed Forces had rocket experts. On the other hand, the conditions prevailing in industry at the time imperiled secrecy. The Army had taken the initiative, and therefore the Army assumed direction of the work. Of course our work could succeed only if we could manage to keep Peenemünde free from excessive red tape and cramping regulations. In that struggle we were engaged without respite throughout our work, and on the whole we were victorious. In my time at Peenemünde, Army Administration and the Experimental Station Branch of the Army Weapons Department had no say.

Later on it would have to be decided whether Peenemünde could, and wanted to, remain permanently in Army hands. The arrangement would work up to the point at which Peenemünde became its own industry and could stand on its own feet. Whether it should eventually be converted into a privately run industrial undertaking, and, if so, when, was a hotly debated question. To do so would not reduce but rather increase the vast subsidies being poured into the development works. A possible advantage was that outstanding specialists and technicians might then be attracted by salaries on the industrial scale. This stage had long been reached with our key men.

However, Peenemünde would still have remained purely a research and development station, in other words, a subsidized enterprise. It could have been associated with a large production works, and by adding development costs to the price of the finished article the enterprise might have been made to pay its way. But what would happen after the war, when only a few missiles were needed? The cost of further development would not be covered.

From the start we had no desire to make money. We wanted to work at research and development. Manufacture would be the concern of heavy industry, and heavy industry could take the profits.

Thus it seemed that the original decision would stand—to maintain Peenemünde as a purely military research and development station. Its later destiny was not to be decided until after the war. But the military situation and the intrigues of power politics forced the Army Weapons Department in June 1944 to abandon these earlier plans of ours.

CHAPTER 26

MY MOST DIFFICULT DECISION

On August 8, 1944, when Himmler appointed SS General Kammler Commissioner General for the A-4 program, it looked as though the struggle for control had come to an end.

I felt like a man who has devoted years of toil and affection to making a superb violin, a masterpiece which needs only tuning, and who then has to look on helplessly while the instrument is grabbed by a tough, unmusical woodman and scraped with a jagged lump of wood. I was in a state of appalling weariness and despair.

In a few words Kammler had been given the powers that were absolutely necessary to carry the program from the development stage to actual operations. I could never have been granted such powers in the conditions then prevailing in Germany. Struggles for dominance within the Armed Forces and between the Ministries, and Hitler's innate distrust of the officer caste, made it impossible. But Himmler was universally feared. After July 20, 1944, he alone in Germany could give orders and distribute powers without let or hindrance.

I had made up my mind to ask to be relieved of my duties and employed elsewhere. One Sunday in August, while I was on leave at home in Bansin, I drafted the application.

That afternoon von Braun and Steinhoff came for coffee. They lectured me for hours, telling me I ought not to leave the undertaking in the lurch at this stage, with the main crisis just coming on. If we wished one day to have a place in the history of technology and receive recognition from the world for our invention of the long-range rocket, I ought not to desert the ship now. I ought at least to stick to the helm as regards technology. I should even try to help Kammler. A layman without inside knowledge could never cope with the technical difficulties of so delicate a mechanism as the rocket, which was not even fully developed. He would be unable, without serious setbacks, to manage the organization built up by my staff, which demanded so much engineering knowledge, tact, and finesse, which was quite unlike anything else and included so many outside departments, institutes, and factories throughout Germany and the occupied territories. If everything did not go as we had planned it, we might expect the collapse of the whole project.

I disagreed. In my opinion they misread the situation. There would be no more negotiating in the program now, no more searching for ways and means. There would be orders, with Kammler's will reigning supreme. I thought I knew my man.

All the more reason, they argued, for trying to save what could be saved. Irrespective of our own views and wishes, the A-4 had to be brought to perfection and delivered fit for action. The organization we had brought into being had to work. There must be no failure. We must not lay ourselves open to blame for any future breakdowns. My colleagues urgently begged me once more not to leave them in the lurch.

My mental conflict was a long one, but through many sleepless nights I fought my way to the decision to stay on. I could see the trouble ahead, the hard and desperate fights with Kammler. I could no longer forcibly impose my own will, for there was no power to back me now. Since the events of July 20, the Army departments at home, right up to the Armed Forces High Command itself, had been cowering before the SS and Himmler. Reluctant they might have been, but they yielded. I could gain nothing with Kammler by persuasion either; he was not open to it.

I knew that the A-4 was still unfinished. There would be complaints and accusations. We should have to work on, making improvements and more improvements. If everything we had achieved so far was not to count for nothing I should have to change my tactics. I would have to offer my assistance. I would have to try to make whatever I wanted look like Kammler's own idea. I would have to put words into his mouth. I would also have to avoid the least appearance of wishing to steal the glory for which he longed so fiercely. I would have to stay in the background. I would have to exploit his position, his energy, and his powers on behalf of the A-4. Everything must seem to happen by his will and desire.

The first two months after Kammler's appointment were hard and bitter ones. I had to endure a whole series of humiliations. I had to submit to a chaotic flood of ignorant, contradictory, irreconcilable orders from this man who was neither soldier nor technician. They took the form of as many as a hundred teletypes a day.

At first I could only look on helplessly while the influence of my staff was weakened by gross interference and efficiency dropped. I also had to stand by calmly as, among my own men, the chaff separated itself from the wheat, and driftwood I had trusted floated over to the opposite bank. In this situation I could let no one share in my innermost plans. I had to stick it out alone until I had won Kammler's confidence and convinced him that I was not dangerous and did not intend to obstruct, criticize, or harm him, but on the contrary could be helpful and useful to him.

In those two months I reached the limit of man's endurance. But I had made rockets my life's work. Now we had to prove that their time had come, and to this duty all personal considerations had to be subordinated.

In the middle of September, Jüttner, now Commander-in-Chief of the Home Front, took a hand. He demanded a clear definition of duties. After long discussion I came to an agreement with Kammler. The order setting out once for all the limits of authority on each side was issued on September 30, 1944, and bore, as a military novelty, three signatures. Jüttner, who knew Kammler, would not sign it until we two had attested by signing ourselves that we regarded the order as binding upon us.

Kammler took over field operations and had power of decision on fundamental questions. I was not made subordinate to him. However, in my own sphere of work I was his permanent representative at home; as inspector of long-range-rocket field units I had control of their formation and training; as his technical staff officer, vested with his own powers, I ran development and supply.

Thus a settlement had been reached which enabled me to remain at my post and which with a little ingenuity on my part might be to the advantage of the long-range rocket—if only there were still time!

Events before this settlement had been exciting enough. On the evening of August 31, I was in Brussels. Here Kammler held his first conference with the Chief of Staff of the Fifteenth Army Corps, the special headquarters detailed by the Armed Forces High Command to direct V-weapon operations. Kammler claimed that he controlled the employment of the A-4, though so far his powers had been limited to the home front. The Fifteenth Army Corps denied his claim and demanded to see an order from the Armed Forces High Command. Kammler had no intention whatever of obtaining or even soliciting one.

On September 8, 1944, when the first V-2 operation against London took place from Holland and Kammler was not in agreement with the measures taken by the commanding officer, Major General Metz, Kammler simply took command himself. Major General Metz withdrew. Kammler became divisional commander of a new special Service division. He had the quickest route to Hitler in his friend Fegelein. Long before the Armed Forces High Command could intervene Kammler had been confirmed in his new post by Hitler. Shortly afterward he achieved independence. By now he had lost interest in the Fifteenth Army Corps, since he had got what he wanted. He had further ambitions, however. At the end of December he took over the "Special Service Army Corps" which hitherto, as the Fifteenth Army Corps, had been directly subordinate to the Armed Forces High Command. General Heinemann promptly resigned. Kammler now stood immediately subordinate to Hitler. He controlled all the V-weapons.

His position was that of a full general. Truly a fantastic career for a man who had never done a single day's military service nor been subjected to any military instruction whatsoever!

He ruthlessly removed all unit commanders who disagreed with him and his methods. A few weeks after the first operation, every staff officer and all unit commanders down to battery level had been changed. Kammler no longer wanted mere batteries for the operations. He wanted whole regiments. The batteries were reorganized into regiments.

From September 4 onward rockets were transported to the front. In September three hundred and fifty were delivered, in October five hundred, then between six hundred and nine hundred every month. Breakdowns occurred. Storage and rain caused the bearing bushings in the servomechanisms to swell. Replacements were not forthcoming. We decided to go in for fast transport. Rockets were no longer stored in the ammunition dumps. Immediately they came off the production line at the Mittelwerk, express transport took them to the front and they were fired within three days. Failures dropped.

Technical teams were detached from Peenemünde to the operational units to help in adjusting newly introduced components. The first echelon of my staff, under Lieutenant Colonel Zippelius, went to the operational area. It looked after transport, delivered the rockets to the batteries, and ran the supply of spare parts.

After this there were hardly any breakdowns and everything seemed to be going smoothly. Development too continued, with the objectives of increasing range, accuracy, and effect.

CHAPTER 27

THE "HEIDEKRAUT" FIRINGS

By the end of July 1944 the situation at Heidelager had become critical. The Russian offensive made it impossible for us to stay there. We found a new firing site some 10 miles east of Tuchel in the dense, extensive forestland of Tuchel Heath. We called the place *Heidekraut* (Heather). We were now firing roughly toward the south.

After the rocket at last went into action on September 6, 1944, the experiments at Heidekraut continued. Despite assertions to the contrary, the A-4 was still not fully developed. Dispersion was too great, effect was unsatisfactory because of the insensitive fuze, and a few rockets still blew up toward the end of the trajectory. We had to eliminate these weaknesses and also to devise optical, acoustic, and radio means of recording the impact, which could no longer be observed from aircraft over the target area. Agents' reports usually came in too late to be used for correction of aim.

Success in the experiments depended on a reasonable supply of rockets for the purpose. The small number of rockets assembled at Peenemünde was not sufficient, and any improvements and new instrumentation had to be incorporated by the Mittelwerk in rockets from the production line.

But we were still getting very few. From August 1944 onward the Mittelwerk produced six hundred rockets a month; the conveyor-belt equipment at the works could have doubled this figure without any trouble. The alcohol bottleneck, however, restricted us considerably. Oxygen also became a restricting factor after the big underground liquefaction plants at Liége and Wittringen in the Saar had been overrun. We reckoned roughly 9 tons of oxygen, which was a day's output for one machine, to one firing. Only about 5 tons remained after the oxygen had been transferred from the factory storage tanks to the railway tank cars of 48-ton capacity, thence to the 5- to 8-ton road tankers, thence to the rocket, where there was loss in the standing time before launching. Thus of every 9 tons produced some 5 tons reached the rocket, which needed 4.96 tons. In the big railway tankers the loss by evaporation was 92 gallons in 24 hours, and in the rocket before launching 4.5 pounds per minute. On the other hand the amount of oxygen available to us in Germany, including what came to us as a by-product of the hydrogen works, did not exceed the output of thirty to thirty-five generators. We therefore had available twenty-eight to thirty rockets per day for military operations and five to seven for test shots and acceptance tests of rocket motors.

The introduction of our experimental rockets into the production line at the Mittelwerk meant delay in delivery of the standard article, and for the first few months I had to struggle with Kammler, who was in charge of operations, every single time an experimental series was needed. For him the only important thing was the number of operational shots. He wanted to report as many as possible to higher authority, and whether they were effective seemed for the moment to be a matter of indifference. At this time we were in constant fear that further development and experimentation would be stopped altogether.

Reports on results gradually began to come in; the withdrawal of the fronts called for longer ranges; as new missile units were formed there was a demand for rockets for training. Kammler then realized that we needed more missiles. But to the very end of operations their number, in relation to the many tasks that still had to be done, was infinitesimally small. The firing of some experimental series was dragged out over weeks. Alterations and improvements took months to come through. On the other hand, the front cried out for faster delivery and higher production. Thus we were no better off. By making some minor improvements in the standard rocket—raising the minimum pressure adjustment and thus raising the average combustion pressure by using the integrating accelerometer instead of the electrical Brennschluss apparatus, and slightly increasing the contents of the tanks—we were able to increase the range of operational rockets to 200 miles. Some experimental missiles with even larger propellant tanks achieved a range of 298 miles when launched from Peenemünde.

We learned from reports in neutral newspapers that in England the rocket had been seen, at the end of its flight, as a red-hot sphere. We had never seen such a thing. Certainly we knew that the dark gray-green camouflage paint could be set on fire by frictional heat, but we had lessened this danger by giving the entire body a coat of graphite paint.

At the end of December 1944 I was paying the last of many visits to Heidekraut. Because of the Russian advance through Poland, I had discussed evacuation with the officer commanding the Training and Experimental Unit, Lieutenant Colonel Moser. He was to go first to the woods south of Wolgast. His target area would then be selected somewhere in the broad, uninhabited region of the Tuchel moors.

The batteries had been operating in bad weather, snow and rain. It was then afternoon and the last rocket was to be launched after dark. The sky cleared. Stars shone brightly as the chilly winter dusk came on. It was nearly eleven before the glow of the exhaust flame reddened the sky. The rocket began its journey. The exhaust, which was alone visible, went through the slow tilting maneuver.

I watched from the platform of a car of our special train at the little station at Lindenbusch, deep in the great Tuchel forest. Brennschluss came at the appointed time. Through my binoculars I could see clearly against the dark sky the small, bright point of light of the white-hot graphite vanes. I wondered how long I would be able to follow the rocket's flight. I had set the stopwatch on my wrist at the moment of take-off, passed it into the car, and was now having the time called out to me.

I could still see the dim point of light after 2 minutes, 3 minutes, 4 minutes. Owing to the curvature of the earth the trajectory seemed very short. Now, after 4 minutes, the point of light was no longer so high in the sky. Not until 4 minutes and 32 seconds had passed did it disappear in the haze of the earth's atmosphere. I had been able to follow the trajectory for over 120 miles.

It seemed to me that I had found the explanation for the rocket's becoming visible during night bombardment. The watchers had seen the glowing graphite of the jet vanes and had mistaken it, owing to the high speed of flight, for the rocket itself.

In the middle of January 1945 Heidekraut had to be evacuated. In deep snow the Training and Experimental Unit, with all its vehicles and equipment, moved to the Wolgast woods, which it left in the middle of February without having managed to fire a single rocket. Their last move was to the neighborhood of Rethen on the Weser, where their aim ran north along the coast of Schleswig-Holstein. But even here no more rockets took off. The time for A-4 practice by the troops was over. On April 3, 1945, Kammler ordered the Training and Experimental Unit to be converted into an infantry battalion for his Army Corps. The order was never carried out.

CHAPTER 28

VARIOUS OTHER ROCKET DEVELOPMENTS

Apart from development of the A-4 itself, Peenemünde and its associated factories were concerned even at this late hour with a number of new possibilities for employing and adapting rocket weapons.

In the autumn of 1943 Lafferenz, of the German Labor Front, paid me a visit and told me that he had proved by actual experiment that, contrary to predictions by the Navy, a submarine could take in tow as many as three cigar-shaped, submersible containers 100 feet long. He urged us to examine the possibility of launching our A-4 from these floats. If it could be done we should be able to bombard big military objectives overseas across hundreds of miles of water.

The problem interested us. In the summer of 1942 we had already experimented near the Greifswalder Oie with launching powder rockets from a submarine. It had been Steinhoff's idea at the time. He had noticed the heavy projectiles developed by my department, the powder rockets for the *Nebelwerfer* detachments. His brother was a submarine commander and was about to start out on a long cruise. We were talking about it and suddenly had an idea. Rockets worked under water; how would it be if we could accommodate twenty or thirty of them, with a charge of inflammable oil or high explosive and ready for launching, aboard a submarine? The submarine could then submerge, approach to within 2 miles of the shore, and discharge the rockets under water against oil-tank installations on the coast. The gasoline and oil tanks would certainly be set on fire by the incendiary rocket warheads, which would ignite on impact.

At Swinemünde improvised launching racks were erected on the deck of the submarine by workmen from Peenemünde, and a few days later several salvos were fired from a depth of 30 to 50 feet. Nothing whatever could be felt of the launchings inside the submerged submarine. The trajectory of the projectiles was excellent, in fact dispersion was reduced and range slightly increased by the initial motion of the missiles through the water, which acted like guide rails. A staggering sight it was when those twenty heavy powder rockets suddenly rose, with a rush and a roar, from the calm waters of the Baltic. This improvisation could have been put to immediate and successful use, but the Naval Weapons Department, the cognizant authority for all naval weapon development, would not approve it, though it had served its purpose perfectly. The Navy had to do its own designing. Months, a whole year went by. The submarine put to sea without rockets. Later on there was no prospect of success because of the short range.

Peenemünde continued its study of the problem posed by Lafferenz. A submarine could tow three floats weighing about 500 tons for 30 days at an average speed of 12 knots. Their submerging and surfacing could be controlled from the submarine. An A-4 and the necessary quantities of propellants could be accommodated without difficulty.

On arrival at the launching point the floats could be partially flooded so that they stood upright in the water. The top hatch could then be opened and the A-4, erect upon its gyro-stabilized platform, after being fueled, prepared for launching, and adjusted, could be discharged.

We did not expect any construction difficulties that could not be overcome, but work on the problem was temporarily suspended because of the A-4 troubles. Now, at the end of 1944, it was resumed. By the middle of December a full memorandum was being prepared on the preliminary experiments, and we were getting to work on the first design sketches. The evacuation of

Peenemünde before the middle of February 1945 put an end to a not unpromising project.

On November 14, 1944, there was tried out at Misdroy on the island of Wollin an experimental constant-pressure gun about 200 feet long, which had been developed by Cönders, an engineer of the firm of Röchling at Saarbrücken. A dune had been given a 45-degree slope for the purpose. The new gun lay without any carriage on wooden and concrete blocks against this slope with no provision for traverse.

My sphere of operations had not, so far, included artillery weapons. However, as Kammler had grabbed all V-weapons, I now had to take an interest in this one as well. The gun had been developed at Hitler's orders, following a proposal by the head of the firm of Röchling. It was to be installed in great numbers underground, in rows, to bombard southern England from the Channel coast with a continuous rain of fin-stabilized projectiles of 6-inch caliber. The gun was called "High-Pressure Pump," "Busy Lizzie," or "Millipede." The barrel was of unalloyed crucible-cast steel. The barrel was made up of a great many T-shaped pieces, each 12 to 16 feet long. With a planned barrel length of nearly 450 feet, the gun was expected to achieve a range of 100 miles. The shell was inserted in the barrel. A base charge, after ignition, provided the first acceleration. As the shell passed the separate T-pieces, the additional powder charges in the lateral arms were ignited one after another, so that the projectile acquired more and more acceleration. An enormous number of gunners was required to service the weapon, standing on the staircases that ran to right and left of the barrel and reloading the T-pieces with powder charges between rounds. It was hoped in this way to fire one round per gun every 5 minutes.

The operational shelter built at Calais for this gun had already been destroyed by bombs and was in Allied hands. Development of the gun was by no means complete. Almost every third shot exploded the barrel somewhere and new T-pieces had to be fitted.

I could only shake my head at the suggestion that this weapon should nevertheless be taken to the front. I was not the only one. Everyone present at the demonstration was agreed that the gun could have no effect whatever on the outcome of the war. But Hitler had ordered experimental work on it to be wound up immediately and demanded its employment at the front. Hence my new job of creating the necessary troop formations and preparing the supply of materials for operations. In January 1945, two short experimental guns with a range of 37 miles were used against Antwerp and the Luxembourg area. But not more than a few shots were fired. Then the guns blew up.

Yet another invention was used prematurely. At Leba, on November 15, 1944, there was a demonstration of a powder step-rocket developed by the firm of Rheinmetall under the direction of Klein and Dr. Vüllers. This missile was called the *Rheinbote*. Rheinmetall had quite correctly reasoned that powder consumption in a long-distance gun with a normal shell and a range of over 75 miles is practically the same as in a powder step-rocket of identical range, and that at greater ranges the powder rocket would give still better results. The problem of excessive weight of the heaviest long-range guns could be reduced to a minimum by employing step-rockets having the same performance. The only fundamental problem was the rocket's extensive dispersion. The missile consisted of four steps, each with stabilization fins. The diameter of the individual steps diminished toward the nose. When the propellant in the first step was exhausted, the second was ignited by a time fuze. The first step then dropped off and the rest of the rocket flew on. When propellant in the remaining steps was exhausted, only the steel casing of the last step, containing the warhead, flew on. This 37-foot rocket could travel 100 miles. The warhead weighed 88 pounds and the high-explosive charge about 45 pounds. The total weight of the rocket was 3773 pounds, including the propellant charge of 1287 pounds. One could be launched every hour.

The Meillerwagen, our long-range-rocket transporter, was used for launching. The boom was converted into a ramp and the hydraulic lifting gear controlled elevation, but there was no travers-

ing mechanism and the vehicle itself had to be turned. This weapon
was by no means fully developed either; its dispersion was very bad
indeed.

Several live rockets were fired from a small pine forest. It was
strange to see the boom of our Meillerwagen, with the long,
slender powder rocket lying on it, jutting out at an angle of 45
degrees above the half-grown trees. The sky was overcast and
heavy rain clouds were driving across it at about 3000 feet. The
first rockets started off well. Ignition of the various steps could be
heard starting at given intervals, together with the deep, gurgling
sound of the steps somersaulting to the ground when they were
burned out. In the third launching, the fins of one step must in
some way have caught in the ramp, for the rocket rose almost
vertically. We ducked involuntarily in our narrow trench. The
different steps were bound to fall on top of us.

After the first three steps had dropped among the pines without
doing any damage, we waited for the fourth and last. It contained
a live warhead. Splinter effect might be dangerous. In a few
minutes we heard the whistle of the falling charge and shortly
afterward its impact on the left flank of the battery. The detonation did not seem very loud. Nothing serious had happened. When
we reached the point of impact we looked at each other in
astonishment and some embarrassment. A small, shallow crater
4 feet wide had been made in the loose sand. Little or no splinter
effect could be traced. And for that, 1300 pounds of powder had
been burned and 2 tons of steel had been thrown all over the
landscape!

We agreed that this weapon, in view of its performance and
slight effect, would be absolutely useless. Yet Hitler and Kammler had ordered it to be employed operationally. Accordingly,
from the beginning of December onward a column of the battery
with two Meillerwagens carried out firings from the area south of
Heidekraut to establish range tables for use at the front. We had
the greatest trouble in finding the impact points at all. As a rule we
failed. The rocket was ordered to be used just the same, and from
the middle of January 1945 a battery was stationed in Holland,

firing against Antwerp Harbor. It was disbanded after shooting about sixty rounds.

When we were considering ways of firing the A-4 right at the beginning of its development, we had thought of using a special railway car as well as the bunker and the cross-country motor vehicle. By the end of 1942 prototypes of the first special railway cars were ready for testing at Test Stand VII at Peenemünde. The idea was to prepare the rocket under cover of a double-tracked tunnel and then drive the transporting and elevating vehicle carrying the firing table to the tunnel entrance. The firing table would be clamped to the rails. The rocket would then be placed on the table by raising the boom, fueled, and fired. Procedure was practically the same as for the motorized units.

Our growing air inferiority in the West and the greater mobility of the motorized units had caused us to suspend this work, but now, at the end of 1944, Kammler demanded its resumption. I had no idea why. Exhaustive tests were carried out at Peenemünde in the last months of the year. I could not believe that there was any point to the work in view of the air situation and I went about it rather half-heartedly. What I had expected happened. In January 1945, after much work had been done, the whole thing was abandoned.

The demand for increased range made it necessary to start work again without delay on the winged A-4, which had been shelved since the spring of 1943. We had named the winged A-4 missile the A-9. Ever since the beginning of the war we had seen that we could not tackle the A-9 as well as the A-4 at Peenemünde with any hope of its also becoming operational in time. The problems would have made far too many demands on our depleted staff. Some research had, however, been done in the wind tunnel since the spring of 1940 to determine the proper shape of the supersonic wings and tail fins of the A-9. The findings were now hastily dug out again and a schedule of tests drawn up.

On January 8, 1945, a first version of the A-9, the A-4 bastard, took off. The control failed about 100 feet above the firing table. A few days later we were unable to launch another missile because the alcohol tank had developed a leak. At last, on January 24, we had our first success. The rocket, climbing vertically, reached a peak height of nearly 50 miles at a maximum speed of 2700 miles per hour. This rocket-powered aircraft, with a wing area of about 145 square feet, broke the sound barrier without trouble. It flew with stability and steered automatically at both subsonic and supersonic speeds. On the descending part of the trajectory, soon after the rocket leveled out at the upper limit of the atmosphere and began to glide, a wing broke. On the whole the result was eminently satisfactory and more than fulfilled our expectations.

Thus our theories on this design had been borne out in this case too. It was possible to cause rocket aircraft to fly at many times the speed of sound, and they could certainly be landed by means of breaking and landing flaps. We were well on the way to solving a problem which, together with high-altitude research, was the first I had set myself to tackle after the war: the landing after a flight into airless space. We had taken a long stride forward in developing the first intermediate stage preceding the spaceship. Rocket aircraft could cover long distances in the upper stratosphere, at heights of 12 to 16 miles, at incredible speed, and still land safely. If only we could succeed in maintaining full rocket thrust just long enough to ensure that we reached this height at very high supersonic speed, flying horizontally and in the right direction, and then either go into a glide or switch on a low-thrust cruising motor using very little propellant, why, then we should be able to bridge thousands of miles in an economically feasible manner. Such were the ideas that occupied our minds in 1944. If we could realize them in practice we might hope to enrich international traffic, a few years after the war, with newer and bigger models. This revolutionary form of transport could never be rivaled for speed and range by normal propeller or jet aircraft.

Basically the problem had already ceased to be a problem. It was only a question of working out the technical details and devoting enough time to development. But the evacuation of Peenemünde put a stop to this experimentation too.

It might be useful to mention at this point to what extent we had considered the use of atomic energy for rocket propulsion. After 1943 we had approached Professor Heisenberg for information about the practical possibilities. He could give us no firm promises of any description.

CHAPTER 29

"V-2 FOR THE FIRST PARTY RALLY
AFTER THE WAR"

I had to turn my attention again to the development of the Wasserfall, the big antiaircraft rocket with which I had long been familiar.

The Wasserfall was fired vertically from a firing table in exactly the same way as the A-4. It was steered visually by remote radio control and was effective within a radius of 16 miles and a height of 11 miles. It was not yet fully developed. The highest speed so far reached was 1350 miles per hour.

The last time I had attended a demonstration of the Wasserfall and other guided missiles had been in the autumn of 1944. That occasion had been a profound shock to me. I must give my reasons for this in some detail.

On that thirtieth of October, 1944, I had to give a short lecture at the firing site of our Wasserfall at Test Stand IX as part of an Air Force demonstration, and if possible fire an A-4 as well.

This time Goering was our guest of honor. After he had greeted the Air Force and Ministry of Munitions people, who had turned up in large numbers, he passed by me on his way to the corrugated metal shed containing models and drawings of the rockets. In my Army uniform I was conspicuous among the Air Force officers. He turned to look at me with a puzzled air. Saur presented me to him, not for the first time.

I had not seen Goering since the spring of 1939, when we had given a demonstration at the Experimental Station at Kummersdorf West. He had changed so much that I could hardly believe

my eyes. Certainly there had been considerably less fuss about
him for the last few years, but he was still Reichsmarshall of
Greater Germany and Commander-in-Chief of the Luftwaffe.

Soft Morocco leather riding boots of glaring red with silver
spurs caught the eye first. Goering was wearing a very heavy and
voluminous greatcoat of Australian opossum with the hairy side
turned outward. As he came toward me, heavily built and walking unsteadily on his small feet so that the open cloak flapped
to one side, I saw his light-gray Air Force uniform with the *Pour
le Mérite* decoration and the Grand Order of the Iron Cross. An
off-white cap and an undress version of the Marshal's baton completed his fantastic get-up. Platinum rings with big rubies gleamed
on his soft, thick-fingered hands. His once energetic features had
grown flaccid, apathetic, and fearfully bloated; his eyes were clear
but restless. He gave the impression of a sated sensualist who had
lost all interest in life. This at a time when our situation in the air
was so desperate, so utterly grim! I felt as though I had received
a blow between the eyes.

The point of the demonstration was to show what stage had
been reached in the development of guided antiaircraft missiles
and to help decide which types to concentrate on.

I went into the shed with Goering. While the various heads of
development described their missiles, Goering walked about
studying the drawings hanging on the wall. Or, rather, he pre-
tended to do so. In fact he was not looking at them at all and had
not the slightest interest. I kept at his elbow. About every five
minutes his eyes began to roll until only the whites were visible.
He would reel, fumble in the pocket of his greatcoat, and swallow
a small pink pill. Then he would suddenly draw himself up again
and seem quite normal. Five minutes later the performance would
be repeated.

He would tap the models and drawings with his baton and call
out "Carry on!" when the lecturer stopped in confusion. It was
an uncanny business. He barely asked one question per lecture.
After half an hour of this he seemed to liven up, put two or three
sarcastic questions, and finished up by saying, "I heard all that

nine months ago. Show me something new!" We went up to the roof of the small Wasserfall Measurement House. As he slowly mounted the outside staircase he drew a heavy revolver from his pocket, threw it up several times, and caught it again. His adjutant finally took it away from him, pointing out that it was loaded and the safety catch off.

About 100 yards in front of the Measurement House four different kinds of rockets stood in a row ready for firing. A few minutes later the first one was fired. The weather was bad. Heavy clouds were crossing the gray sky about a mile up and in a few seconds all the rockets had vanished beyond them. There was no possible means of telling whether the remote-control sets had the slightest influence on the rockets. Goering lost his temper and shouted, "If that's all you've got to show me, you can go to the devil! I saw it all a year ago and exactly the same thing happened then."

He came down the staircase again, caught sight of me, and asked, "When are *you* going to shoot? I want to see the V-2."

On the way to the Measurement House I had pointed out to him an A-4 rocket set up in the woods with its vehicles and said a few words about its range and accuracy. Goering had seemed a changed man. He had laughed, beamed all over his face, and insisted on examining the huge weapon from all sides.

"In an hour's time, according to the program. We are ahead of time with the demonstration and shan't be ready to fire straight away," I told him.

"Well, get on with it. The things they're trying to show off to me here are just a lot of stale gadgets they can't finish."

After half an hour spent in conference he again emerged from the Measurement House. Meanwhile I had been trying to hurry the launching preparations. There were still 10 minutes to go. Goering asked, "Where's the rocket?"

"For safety's sake we've put it back there in the woods, five hundred yards away. You can't see it from here."

He stamped his foot. "But I want to see it!"

"When it's launched it will rise slowly above the trees. Then you'll be able to see it perfectly."

He raised his enormous binoculars and looked in the direction I had indicated.

"The rocket rises quite slowly at first. There's no need for field glasses until you see it coming up."

Goering behaved like an excited little boy. He kept putting up his binoculars. At last a dense cloud of smoke rose above the woods. The rumble of the preliminary stage became audible. Then with a thunderous roar the rocket rose straight into the air. The tilt began and the missile vanished eastward into the clouds.

Goering turned round, laughing. His vast cloak came flapping round me. He seized me in his arms, thumped me on the back, and said, "That's terrific! We must have that at the first Party Rally after the war!"

This on October 30, 1944! I was speechless.

Goering wanted to see a second launching. We had prepared a second rocket in case the first failed, but it could not be fired for at least an hour. Goering had the top of his car pushed back, ordered someone to come with him and show him where to keep looking out for the rocket, and was then driven, looking over his shoulder, to the Air Force Experimental Station at Peenemünde West.

When I arrived there an hour later Goering was standing in front of the great hangars damaged by the air raid. Dr. Kramer of the Ruhr Steel Company was talking to him about a small wire-controlled air-to-air rocket, the X-4.

Goering at once rushed up to me. "When do you start? Where can I see the rocket from?"

I assured him that in about 10 minutes he would be able to see everything quite clearly from where he stood. Unwillingly he simmered down. Binoculars in hand, he paced impatiently up and down on the green lawn in front of the hangar. He only half listened while the anxious Kramer continued his exposition.

"Reichsmarshall, I must have your approval today for giving the X-4 top priority from now on. I must have it or we shall never finish developing it."

How often had I used precisely the same words myself! I could easily imagine Kramer's feelings. He was fighting the same battle that had been forced upon me for years. I knew that what he said was true.

Goering merely answered, with a smile of resignation, "What's the point of my agreeing? Before I get home some department of my General Staff is certain to have reversed my decision. I've no say nowadays in my own outfit."

Our second launching, too, made Goering clap his hands with delight. He cursed his own development staff and finally said, "Why is it that this fellow manages all right and you don't? Let him show you how it ought to be done!"

Poor old Luftwaffe!

After that he drove away.

CHAPTER 30

"WORKING STAFF DORNBERGER"— TOO LATE!

The situation in the air went from bad to worse. An incessant stream of bombers roared over Germany day and night. Our successes in defense meant relatively less and less. It could only be a question of time before all our cities, factories, and centers of communication lay in ruins.

Every time a bomber formation roared overhead I was seized with impotent rage at the shortsightedness shown from the outbreak of war by those responsible for our air armaments, and at the utter inability to realize the weakness of our industrial war potential compared with that of the United States.

How many things we had tried to develop and introduce! As early as 1939 von Braun had designed a rocket interceptor capable of rising to a height of 35,000 feet in 60 seconds, to be vertically launched, piloted, and remote-controlled until it reached the level of the bomber formation to be attacked. I can still see the disdainful smiles on the faces of the Air Ministry officials when our proposal was finally rejected in the autumn of 1941.

"Our fighters will look after air defense!" That had settled it. Even then I knew that the time was not far off when they would be crying out for these weapons and want them all to be ready in five minutes.

The same shortsightedness had also prevented the final development and mass production of a German antitank rocket that could be operated by a single man. In February 1942, after the first big setbacks in Russia, I had proposed such a weapon. We had carried out the necessary tests with rocket projectiles carrying shaped charges. All we needed to manufacture hundreds of thousands of these cheap weapons was the approval of the Infantry Board. The Infantry Board rejected the idea. They declared it impossible to equip front-line infantry with a rocket weapon because it would instantly be spotted and put out of action. It was not until the American bazooka proved itself conclusively on the Tunisian front that hesitation was thrown to the winds and the *Panzer-schreck* and *Panzerfaust* were hastily developed.

The air situation grew more and more desperate. Then, at the beginning of December 1944, Professor Petersen, head of the Long-Range Weapons Commission, suffered a stroke. Shortly afterward I was asked to go and see the head of the Development Department at the Ministry of Munitions. On behalf of Speer, the Minister, Colonel Geist, asked whether I would take over the commission.

Only a year before it had been declared impossible for me, as an Army officer, to be granted ministerial powers in connection with my A-4 program and to give orders to organizations within the Ministry of Munitions. Now, as they no longer knew how to proceed, I was to pull their irons out of the fire. Since the problem had become insoluble it was to be passed to me. I declined. I gave as my reason that I was not *au courant* and did not intend to lead a ministerial commission of first-class men. Geist begged me to think the matter over and let him know my decision within the next few days.

I mentioned the idea to von Braun. He seemed to know all about it. I had the impression that he had been asked to persuade me to agree. But I had the gravest doubts. I was unshakably convinced that the war was lost and that it could only be a question of months before the final collapse. Nothing could be achieved in so short a time with so cumbersome a tool as this commission.

Von Braun suggested that the commission should be sent home and a working group be formed from a few engineers and scientists actually engaged in development and research. I could use my post at the Ministry of Munitions to push through what could still be done. That appealed to me. I needed people round me who spoke my own language, people who really worked, people who could seek help from me and find it readily, thanks to my experience and official position. In a word, for a problem like this I needed engineers—men of action, not committeemen.

Finally we agreed, despite my doubts about the time left to us, to form a so-called working group. At the end of December I had another interview with Geist, who said he would talk to the Minister.

On January 12, 1945, at Speer's orders, "Working Staff Dornberger" was set up as part of the Development Department of the Ministry of Munitions with the object of breaking Allied air superiority. Its ten members were all men of practical experience. If the situation could be saved at all, these experts were the men to do it.

Alas, we had forgotten Kammler. The Ministry of Munitions, the only organization that still put up any resistance to him, had not invited him to the preliminary talks. When he heard of my appointment he immediately induced Goering to make him Special Commissioner for "Breaking the Air Terror." Some plain speaking followed. Then, without further ado, he appointed me and my working group to be his technical staff in his new capacity! He had finally come to realize that he would be unable to direct the technical side in addition to all his other duties.

This double appointment gave me great advantages. From the Ministry of Munitions I could direct civil authorities and industry to take whatever steps we thought necessary, and as Kammler's executive I had similar powers vis-à-vis the military authorities. We were now in charge of all V-weapons and all antiaircraft development except actual AA guns. Now at long last, in these final months of the war, I possessed the powers I had so long dreamed of and vainly fought for in connection with the A-4.

Yet I felt ill at ease. It was too late. The problem was now insoluble. I felt morally certain that we had only a few months left and that nothing we did could affect the issue decisively. The iniquity of that stubborn, foolish order, repeated with deadly inevitability every spring in exactly the same terms, that all planning which could not be completed by autumn was to be scrapped, could not now be atoned for.

Any long-term development dictated by foresight and involving the latest technical discoveries had for years been possible only "under the counter." The errors and neglect of high authority were now irremediable. All we could do was to create priorities, giving precedence to what was simple and could be quickly mass-produced, and so try to give the forces a little breathing space.

The worsening of the air situation, the long distances between the centers of development and those of production, and the obstacles to transport and travel were crippling hindrances to fast work. We also had to overcome at first some active and passive resistance from departments and factories which, understandably, did not take kindly to directions from an unfamiliar source.

I set myself at once to get a clear picture of work in progress and its prospects. I sent for heads of development sections of the various weapons departments, toured the factories myself, and dispatched members of my working group everywhere for information. The urgency was imperative, a matter of life and death.

The powers I possessed enabled me to build up the picture in a relatively short time. There was, for instance, the development that had been going on since the spring on nonguided antiaircraft rockets for use either from the ground or from aircraft. Once before I had given effective help to the antiaircraft effort without reference to the proper authority, the Air Force. With a little cooperation on both sides the same thing could surely be done again through the usual channels.

On that occasion a short, slim Air Force major from the front had turned up at my Berlin office. He had seen the Nebelwerfer on the eastern front and now asked me whether it could be mounted on the fighters in his squadron. He said his superior officers did not know he was taking this step. Could we do it on the q.t.?

Here was a windfall for me! At last, I thought!

Years before we had developed a 6-centimeter rocket armament for fighters in my branch of the Army Weapons Department, but it had been regularly turned down by the Air Ministry. This caliber was too small for the young major. He wanted really big rockets with time fuzes so that the explosive charge would detonate among the enemy bomber squadrons, scattering them and giving his fighters a much better chance in the action to follow.

Twenty minutes later I was on my way to Kummersdorf in my car with the major and a departmental officer. I at once had four launching tubes taken out of a 21-centimeter Nebelwerfer and sent for eight rounds with suitable time fuzes. Not many hours later the major, highly delighted,. drove off again with the experimental launchers and fittings which had been adapted to his purpose in the workshops. Two days later he rang me up to report that the first experiments had been successful.

In no time we had delivered enough launchers and ammunition for several fighter squadrons. They were first used during the big Allied raids on Schweinfurt in January 1944 and thoroughly proved their worth in the air tactics prevailing at that time.

In June 1944 I had a remarkable and significant experience with remote-controlled antiaircraft rockets launched from the ground.

I was rung up at Heidelager from Hitler's headquarters and asked whether any A-4 had been fired from Peenemünde in the last few days. I called up Peenemünde and received a negative reply. The Air Force also stated that they had not been firing their Fi-103, the V-1.

Someone, however, must have been firing. A mysterious, remote-controlled missile had exploded in southern Sweden some thousands of feet above the ground. A great deal of sheet metal and fragments of apparatus had been found scattered over a wide area. It looked very much as if they were talking about an A-4 airburst.

I again telephoned Peenemünde. I was then told that a missile had been fired, but not to any distance. They had merely been testing the remote-control equipment for the big Wasserfall antiaircraft rocket mounted in an A-4, and the projectile had gone astray.

Close inquiry revealed that while the rocket was still traveling slowly the control engineer had changed its direction by eye and lost contact with it when it unexpectedly moved sideways into low cloud. The engineer had tried to bring the rocket back but evidently failed because of the cloud cover. The rocket had gone on flying north, which unluckily took it to southern Sweden. It had, moreover, been fully fueled so that thrust had lasted until the propellants were completely consumed.

I reported all this to headquarters. On being asked whether conclusions about the rocket, its performance, and the way it worked, might be drawn from the pieces, I answered yes. I answered no to a further question whether I thought a replica could be made quickly, thus enabling the Allies to develop jamming methods. I felt confident enough to add the assurance that the Wasserfall control equipment would give the enemy's intelligence service some hard nuts to crack and might lead to false conclusions.

Although I had had absolutely nothing to do with the test I was summoned to the Führer's headquarters to receive a reprimand, with the consoling comment that Hitler was in a towering rage. I flew to Rastenburg, but by the time I arrived the storm had subsided. Hitler had changed his mind. It seemed there had been some sort of row with the Swedes. At any rate, Jodl told me when I reported to him that I might take myself off again. Hitler had declared that it was quite a good thing for the Swedes to realize that we could bombard their country from Germany; they would be more inclined to be cooperative in negotiations.

CHAPTER 31

GÖTTERDÄMMERUNG OVER GERMANY

On January 27, 1945, the whole "Working Staff Dornberger" met in Berlin for the first time. The situation and prospects were horribly depressing, but I felt we had gathered enough material to give me an unvarnished picture of the truth.

We reviewed a great many projects, none yet complete and all requiring months of steady application before their usefulness could be definitely established. Besides nonguided antiaircraft powder rockets, there was a multitude of plans for remote-controlled missiles with solid- or liquid-propellant rocket propulsion to be launched either from the ground of from aircraft. Some of the arrangements for remote control were still in their infancy, and visual guidance remained the rule for the time being. There was no early prospect of using the missiles at night or in overcast weather.

With nearly all these projects the initial idea had been to guide the missile to its target automatically on the same radio beam that located the aircraft, as in beam-guided flight. The shortwave system that was to be used was still not practicable. Instead the rockets were to be visually guided by radio control until they were close to the bomber formation. An acoustic or radar homing mechanism would take over 2 miles from the target and a proximity fuze detonate the charge on close approach. But even these mechanisms had not got beyond the stage of laboratory models, though the latter had been shown to be workable. In no case had they been mounted in a rocket and tested against flying targets.

We found great overlapping both of government departments and industry on guided antiaircraft rockets of practically identical performance. Little groups of people scattered all over Germany were busy on such tasks, often with wholly inadequate resources, while transport difficulties grew daily more acute.

So these were the Government's famous "wonder weapons" so long trustingly awaited by the German people! In the few months that could be left to us in the prevailing military situation they could not even postpone the catastrophe, much less turn the scales.

This bitter truth and the whole gravity of the position had to be brought home with all emphasis to high authority, and all delusive hopes firmly trodden upon. I had a talk with Kammler. I told him what I had found and gave him a complete list of the various types of weapons, showing their performance, delivery dates, and potentialities. Whether there was any point in our continuing work at all, I said, depended on how much time we had left. We were going to have to ask where and for how long the Government believed it could resist the Allies now converging from both sides on central Germany.

Kammler did not fail to appreciate the gravity of the position, but he was even then incomprehensibly optimistic. He thought we could still count on at least 6 months to get our weapons into action, but even that would be too short to get real results. In this situation it was fatal to go on with so many projects. We should have to cut and combine ruthlessly.

If work was to go on with the slightest prospect of success we should have to move in good time all factories, technical institutes, and development centers likely to be in the battle area within the next few months. The delays this would involve would have to be accepted unless we were prepared to write off entire undertakings in advance.

We cut. In the end all the guided antiaircraft rockets we had left were a ground-controlled missile, flying at subsonic speed—the "Butterfly" of the Henschel Aircraft Works, developed by Professor Wagner; another missile of this kind, but for use at supersonic speed; the Peenemünde Wasserfall; and last, the X-4, a small, aircraft-projected, wire-controlled missile, developed by Dr. Kramer of the Ruhr Steel Company. Only one type of homing device and fuze might be worked on for each. All the firms concerned were to be evacuated to the Nordhausen-Bleicherode area in Thuringia, and their staffs reinforced by men released from other duties under the new arrangements.

The move began early in February. My own staffs also moved from Schwedt on the Oder to the southern slopes of the Harz Mountains near Bad Sachsa. All other firms in our program as well as the Service departments, whether Army or Air Force, were evacuated to the same area. In prevailing conditions this seemed the only way we could hope to direct and assist development, call conferences at short notice, and make known our decisions without delay.

We were able to work like this for a month. After that, however, it must have been quite clear even to the humblest mechanic that none of these guided antiaircraft rockets would ever go into action. Even if the High Command had succeeded in holding the Americans and British on the Rhine and the Russians on the Vistula, bombing alone would have delayed until the spring of 1946 delivery of any of the rockets in sufficient quantity to protect vital objectives in the front line and at home and give any substantial relief in the air war. Not until then, and until we had achieved remote control at night and in cloudy weather, could we have hoped slowly to regain command of the air over Germany.

We lacked 18 months of development at top priority. We lacked the lost years between 1939 and 1942.

Kammler refused to believe in an imminent collapse. He dashed to and fro between the Dutch and Rhineland fronts and Thuringia and Berlin. He was on the move day and night. Conferences were called for 1 o'clock in the morning somewhere in the Harz Mountains, or we would meet at midnight somewhere on the Autobahn and then, after a brief exchange of views, drive back to work again. We were prey to terrific nervous tension. Irritable and overworked as we were, we didn't mince words. Kammler, if he got impatient and wanted to drive on, would wake the slumbering officers of his suite with a burst from his tommy-gun. "No need for *them* to sleep! I can't either!" Fixed working hours and leisure had long been things of the past.

Twilight of the Gods! In the gloomy atmosphere pervading all Germany it was infinitely hard for me, who knew the technical facts and the uselessness of it all, not to leave my colleagues and my work in the lurch.

Kammler still believed that he alone, with his Army Corps and the weapons over which he had absolute authority, could prevent the imminent collapse, postpone a decision, and even turn the scales. The transporters still moved without respite to the operational area. Convoys of motor vehicles bridged the gaps in the railways. Kammler's supply columns, equipped with infrared devices that enabled them to see in the dark, rumbled along the Dutch highways.

When the only railway supply line to The Hague firing base had been blown up by Dutch resistance groups and the local commander was short of men to protect it, Kammler took over with reserve and training units brought overnight from Germany, together with improvised contingents of the launching troops. He managed to hold the line clear. But what were the exertions of a single berserk warrior and his weak detachments against the menace advancing irresistibly from the west with a power beyond calculation?

The V-weapon corps continued to engage the Allies until the end of March. Its losses were very light. Then Kammler, completely misreading the military situation, turned it into an infantry corps and hoped, by transferring it to the Harz area, to be able to prevent a junction of the American and Russian armies.

His corps had bombarded London, southern England, and Antwerp with V-weapons from bases in Holland until March 27. V-1's had also taken part in the Rhineland and Ardennes fighting. When the V-1's could no longer reach southern England because of our withdrawal, the weapons were launched from aircraft. Ninety-three hundred V-1's had been fired, day and night, against England alone. About six thousand had reached the English coast. Tens of thousands were earmarked against other objectives. Forty-three hundred V-2's had so far been operationally launched. About fifteen hundred had been directed against England and over twenty-one hundred against Antwerp Harbor. Some 20 per cent were beam-guided.

By the end of March we had increased the V-1 range to 230 miles, though only at experimental stations. Only a few of these new V-1's were used at the front; trimming controls enabled them to change direction. Instead of keeping a straight course they flew in a wide curve and thus hampered the defenses. Still greater ranges of up to 300 miles were planned for a new model in the closing stage of development.

The effective range of most A-4's had been increased to 220 miles, and such rockets had been in action for months. After the latest improvements based on the Heidekraut tests there had been practically no more airbursts.

Before March was out, however, the end had come for this new weapon of war. Holland had to be evacuated and the launching bases were lost to us. Kammler, when he saw this coming, changed his policy. At the end of February he had himself appointed by Hitler to be the latter's "General Commissioner for Turbojet Fighters." Once again he believed that with these machines he could still turn the tide.

For more than a year past we had been mass-producing gas-turbine jet engines in the underground galleries of the Mittelwerk, but only a very small number of jet fighters had so far been in action. An incomprehensible conflict had raged over their operational use. For years there had been argument whether the Messerschmitt Me-262 should be a bomber or a fighter.

Kammler needed effective weapons for them quickly. The guided antiaircraft rockets for launching from aircraft were not yet ready. I was ordered to produce a rocket weapon which could be rapidly manufactured and provisionally mounted, ready for immediate use, on the Me-262.

In a few days I dashed at breakneck speed through the steadily shrinking remnants of Germany, going from test station to test station, from airfield to airfield, from factory to factory. I drove through crowds of civilian refugees from East Prussia and Pomerania, fleeing before the oncoming Russians. I saw misery and unspeakable destitution. I drove through burning towns and villages in Brandenburg and Mecklenburg, past wrecked railways and factories. I met hardly a single truck or car on either secondary or main roads. It was as though time had gone back 75 years. Only horses, wheelbarrows, and people were to be seen. I heard hardly any complaints and yet I shall never forget the eyes of those desperate people.

Once, while we were testing one of our defensive weapons on the little auxiliary airfield at Parchim in Mecklenburg, we had to suspend the work while squadron after squadron of Allied bombers passed overhead at a few thousand feet. In the very far distance we heard the rolling thunder of the bombs. The earth trembled.

Well camouflaged and dispersed under clumps of trees surrounding the airfield stood many hundreds of the latest fighters. Not one took off. I asked in despair why on earth the squadrons were not engaging the enemy, why, since the bombers were flying so low and so close, no attempt was made to risk an action with the many new weapons being tested here. The little Air Force major, who wore the Knight's Cross of the Iron Cross with Oak Leaves, sadly replied, "Sir, I've just enough gasoline to get me to a conference tonight two miles away. For my machines there isn't a single drop."

As here, so at all the stations where our fighters stood ready by the hundreds and thousands. We had no more fuel. Yet the mass production of fighters that could never take off went steadily on in the underground factories.

Was there in Germany really no one in high places with the courage, in this manifestly hopeless situation, to make an end at last? Did no one dare to declare openly that the war was lost?

On March 12, 1945, I made a last proposal based on the information I had gleaned. There were only four available weapons that might be suitable and could be produced in sufficient numbers in a short time. They could not win a war but if they were used in concentration in one area they might perhaps give some temporary relief.

One was the R-4M, a 2-inch powder rocket with tail surfaces that could be folded back. As many as forty-eight of these missiles could be carried on the underwing racks of a fighter and fired practically simultaneously against a bomber formation at a range of 1200 to 1500 yards, so that excellent results could be expected. A single hit with the 1-pound charge would be quite enough to bring down a bomber. In its first operational use in Messerschmitt Me-109's this weapon had already proved its worth. It was being mass-produced at Lübeck by the German Weapons and Munitions Works.

Next we had good secondary armament in the shape of a small recoil-less mortar which was optically triggered. In air combat, when the airplane's silhouette appeared on a selenium cell, the shell was discharged, depending on the mounting of the weapon in the airplane, either straight upward, straight downward, or laterally. The projectile weighed 15 pounds, was 2 inches in diameter, and traveled at 1300 feet per second. Our very fast jet turbine fighters would be able to bring the weapon to bear by flying directly above or below the Allied bomber formations.

We also had small explosive bodies, suspended on wires 250 yards long, and which were brought slowly to earth by means of small parachutes. They could be dropped in masses ahead of the bomber formation, thus forming an effective barrage. Lastly, there were canisters which could be filled with hundreds of little explosive and incendiary bombs. Everything else was either at too early a stage of development or could not be produced immediately.

These weapons, then, were available, but their employment could only be effective if enough Me-262's could be concentrated at a single point and armed with one or another of them, as choice might dictate. We never managed it. A concentration of flying formations was no longer possible.

On April 3, 1945, I had orders from Kammler to evacuate my staff of four hundred and fifty old Peenemünde men to the Lower Alps near Oberammergau. We moved on April 6, as the American tanks advanced through Bleicherode toward Bad Sachsa. From that time onward we were accompanied by SD men. I suspected what that meant. Were we to be used as hostages in armistice negotiations? Or were we to be prevented from falling into Allied hands? Either way it didn't really matter.

I parted from Kammler and spent the last month of the war at Oberjoch near Hindelang with my staff and Professor von Braun, who had been injured in an automobile accident. All development work had stopped. We lay on the terrace of our quarters and let the sun beat down on us. We gave ourselves up to our thoughts, argued about our more important projects, and slowly achieved detachment from the march of events.

About us towered the snow-covered Allgäu Mountains, their peaks glittering in the sunlight under the clear blue sky. Far below us it was already spring. The hill pastures were a bright green. Even on our high mountain pass the first flowers were thrusting buds through the melting snow. It was so infinitely peaceful here! Had the last few years been nothing but a bad dream? The war was over and with it had ceased for years, perhaps for decades, possibly forever, all further work in Germany in our field of endeavor: big long-range rockets, stratosphere aircraft, the first step toward the spaceship, the advance into the universe.

As so often before in the history of technology, necessity in Germany after the First World War had forced a great invention to proceed by way of weapon development. Never would any private or public body have devoted hundreds of millions of marks to the development of long-range rockets for purely scientific purposes. Even with a view to intercontinental traffic the whole idea was still too vague and uncertain to attract the huge sums that were inescapably involved. At the time we began our work the long-range rocket could have shown no sort of profit for decades; if we wanted to forge ahead this was the one possible way.

The military importance of the long-range rocket as a weapon can be, and will be, doubted and belittled. It will be said that we should have produced more fighters and bombers instead of the A-4. The reproach is a foolish one and can easily be refuted. The fighter program, which began too late, went on at full speed right up to the closing days of the war. We lacked not fighters but gasoline. Our vital artery, fuel, had run dry.

For our long-range rocket we needed no petrol; we had our own fuel. The protection of hydrogenation plants should have been the main task of our air defenses. It was neglected, and because the importance of guided antiaircraft rockets was recognized too late, the neglect could not be made good when the situation became critical.

The rocket will be stigmatized as too expensive. This objection, too, merely obscures the issue. Every A-4 in mass production cost thousands of marks less than a torpedo and less than a thirtieth of the price of a twin-engined bomber. And how often, after 1941, could a German bomber fly to England before being shot down?

The operational use of the A-4 at an imperfect stage of development will also be called pointless, brutal, and inhuman, but all long-range artillery and bombing must accept the same condemnation. The spread of the V-2 in relation to its range was always less than that of bombs and big guns.

We were well aware that operational employment of the A-4 in the autumn of 1944 could not of itself win the war. But what would have happened if, during the period since the summer of 1942, by day and night, more and more long-range rockets with ever-increasing range, accuracy, and effect had fallen on England?

It is idle to speculate on this. Only one thing can be said with absolute certainty: the use of the V-2 may be aptly summed up in the two words "too late." Lack of foresight in high places and failure to understand the scientific background were to blame.

We also know, however, that what we created was new and unique and can never be erased from the annals of technology. We tackled one of mankind's great tasks regardless of circumstances and found a first practical solution; we opened the gate and pointed the way to the future.

By gathering together in one place young, enthusiastic, and steadfast scientists, engineers, and technicians in the most varied fields and providing scientific and technical installations on a generous scale, we successfully tackled, in isolation from "the dynamic of events" around us, problems whose solution seemed to lie far in the future. We developed rocket propulsion to a practically unimagined level of performance, applied high-speed aerodynamics on a big scale, and gave guidance technique the dominant place in our work that properly belonged to it. The long-range rocket owes its birth no less to the intelligent exploitation of these three new branches of technology than to the skill, enthusiasm, and cooperation of the men engaged in the project.

We are proud of our technical achievements. In those days of quiet meditation at Oberjoch, when I recalled the time when we were developing the A-4 long-range rocket and let all the discoveries, images, and impressions of the years from 1930 to 1945 unfold again in my mind's eye, I was filled with boundless happiness and gratitude.

Neither the V-2 nor the V-1, nor any other great technological invention of recent decades, can be associated with the name of any one man. The days of the lonely creative genius are over. Such achievements can only be the fruit of an anonymous team of research specialists working selflessly, soberly, and in harmony. In the history of modern technology it can seldom have been given to a handful of men starting from nothing to reach in so short a time a conclusion so technically advanced, so revolutionary, and offering such infinite possibilities.

Ignoring the rocket as a weapon of war, its general potentialities are enormous. A dream can now become reality; the spaceship can emerge out of hopes and theories. To this our labor, our creation, and our success made the first contributions. It must be left to the victors in this, let us hope, last great war, to see that our contribution is not lost.

INDEX

INDEX